Wild Oats
and
Wellingtons

Best wishes

Fordyce Maxwell

Wild Oats
and
Wellingtons

Fordyce Maxwell

Drawings by Turnbull of the
Glasgow Herald

Bridge Studios
Northumberland
1990

First published in Great Britain in 1990

by Bridge Studios,
    Kirklands,
    The Old Vicarage,
    Scremerston,
    Berwick upon Tweed,
    Northumberland.
    TD15 2RB

    Tel. 0289 302658/330274

ISBN 1 872010 55 5

Typeset by EMS Phototypesetting,
Hide Hill, Berwick upon Tweed.

Printed by Martin's of Berwick Ltd.

To farmers everywhere

Acknowledgements

The stories in this collection are reproduced by kind permission of *The Scotsman*, the *Glasgow Herald*, the *Scottish Farmer*, the Tweeddale Press Group and *The Journal*, Newcastle upon Tyne.

Foreword

I share a habit with most newspaper readers of earmarking a good article, saying 'I must cut that out and keep it', then laying the paper aside meaning to retrieve it later.

By the time I remember, the newspaper has been used to light a fire, carry away the ashes from the previous one, to make a papier mâché mask for the school play or line a box for a pet lamb.

This anthology gives readers the chance to catch up on years of missing articles, although perhaps anthology is the wrong word, conjuring up as it does Eng. Lit., *The Golden Treasury* and long-ago classrooms.

This collection is nothing like that. It is journalism on the hoof, farming as I found it and as it happened. There was no time to polish nuggets of prose, no guarantee that the result would have been any better if I had.

A journalist is always preparing to move on to the next thing and this was doubly true when I was farming in partnership with two brothers.

Many articles were written not only under the pressure of an approaching deadline, but also the farming deadlines of a late night lambing shift, a farrowing, ploughing or drilling to be done, grain to be harvested or simply the need to get to bed.

As with *A Farmer's Lot...* most of them try to reflect the lighter side of farming. I think it is instructive that in recent years I have not been alone in trying to do that. We have had a plethora of books doing it and I believe that this is in inverse proportion to how hard it is to make a living from farming.

In palmier days farming books tended to be serious, heavy stuff for the professional, big on gross margins and variable and fixed costs and actuarial values for fertiliser residues. The heavy stuff is still there, but the emphasis is on trying to raise a smile from the weary professional and punter with a passing interest alike.

Apart from the purely frivolous, silly and downright twee productions, honesty comes into it. There is that fine dividing line between being admired for your honesty and being dismissed as an incompetent idiot.

Now that I'm back in full-time journalism all I can say is that I was there in the 70s and 80s, one of those periodic rise and fall periods for British farming.

A Farmer's Boy was what farming was like in the 1950s and early 1960s. This collection, in its own way, gives a clear view of farming in the 1970s and 1980s and a hint of what is in store in the 1990s.

That is five decades, a much longer time than I care to think about to be at the sharp end. No doubt there is many a sombre message to be learned from these decades, but you'll be lucky to find them in here.

I can do no better than leave the final introduction for this book to one of my own favourite authors, Mark Twain, by quoting his foreword to *Huckleberry Finn*: 'Persons attempting to find a motive in this narrative will be prosecuted; persons attempting to find a moral in it will be banished; persons attempting to find a plot in it will be shot.'

All for a fiver

'Right,' said the wages inspector, 'I've met and talked to your shepherd and stockman and your son does most of the tractor work. Is that your total staff, or is there anyone else?'

'Well,' said the farmer, 'there is the half-wit. No, that's not quite fair, not a half-wit, but you know,' tapping his forehead significantly, 'only nineteen bob in the pound. Or 95p metricated.'

'I see,' said the inspector, perking up visibly. 'And, er, does he, you know, do much – I mean, he does, er, actually work?'

Casually, he poised his Civil Service issue ballpoint over his BBC-type clipboard like a nervous journalist trying to get a quote from a Clydesdale breeder beaten into second place.

'Work!' said the farmer, 'Work! Man, he puts in twelve hours a day regular. He's at it first thing in the morning before anybody else and he's still going when a'body else has loused for the night.'

'Damn,' said the inspector in a momentary panic as his ballpoint seized up. Then it started flowing again and his scribbling caught up with the evidence.

The farmer puffed thoughtfully on his battered briar and looked at the frantic scribbling. He pointed to a word with a stubby, calloused finger:

'The word's loused, not decontaminated – it means knocking-off, clocking off, finished for the day.'

'Thank you,' said the inspector, only slightly flustered, crossing it out with a flourish. 'You learn something new every day, eh?'

'You're welcome,' said the farmer.

9

'Now this, er, 95 pence chappie, he works at least twelve hours a day, you say?'

'Oh,' said the farmer, 'that's in the quiet spells. Busy times he's hardly in bed: running messages, driving the spare tractor, carting bales, filling in at lunch times, answering the phone, loading wagons, emptying wagons.

'He rolls the fleeces at the clipping, does most of the odd joinery work about the place, feeds the stock at weekends.'

The ballpoint was flying over the page. 'I see,' said the inspector, his eyes glittering, 'a handy chap to have around?'

'Oh, aye, handy enough when he has to be,' said the farmer,' and he usually has to be. A bit lacking but usually willing and even when he isn't willing, well, we keep him at it.'

The inspector was beginning to look like a man who had lost a washer and picked up a ten pound note. He could barely believe his luck had turned after what had really been a boring day – a tidy, well-run farm, a fairly contented staff, but now this.

It only showed you had to persevere and ask all the questions in this job. Some people would try to get away with murder.

He looked sideways at the farmer's open, weatherbeaten features as he contentedly smoked his pipe with one eye on dark clouds building up on the horizon.

'Well now,' he said, checking his clipboard carefully, 'that's quite a range of activities for an alleged half-wit.'

'Oh, that's not all,' the farmer replied. 'Whiles we turn him loose on the paperwork. It's little short of amazing the way he gets through it, considering his mental capabilities.'

'Times, of course, we get nasty letters back from the VAT office, and once or twice we've had a bit of trouble with the stock movement book, and there was a barley cheque went missing for two months until we found he'd stuck it in his overall pocket and it had been washed twice, but all in all, he manages.'

The inspector was almost whimpering with excitement. 'And, er, of course the crunch question, you do pay him commensurate with his efforts?'

'No, usually Bank of Scotland notes. But not many of them. He gets the occasional fiver, maybe once or twice a month when we let him away for the night.'

This was it. The inspector had felt it all along. He had him now. An employer of the worst type, capitalising on incapacity and the poor exploited devil of a half-wit would never realise it.

A tear dimmed the inspector's eye, Downtrodden, exploited, neglected, working his life away, and given an occasional fiver for a night-out to drown his sorrows.

It was time for the heavy-mob act. 'Well now,' he said in his heavy-mob voice, 'I must say this is an appalling situation, quite one of the worst I've had to deal with in twenty years' experience. He does all this and you give him an occasional – and I quote your very words – an occasional fiver.'

The farmer nodded pleasantly, 'Ah,' he said, 'and the occasional half ounce of baccy, and he lives in.'

'But,' cried the inspector, 'this man is worth £100 a week at least from what you've told me yourself!'

'More, I'd say,' agreed the farmer. 'A hundred pounds is a conservative estimate when you see what some folk make in other jobs, like the Civil Service.'

'All right,' said the inspector, ignoring the last remark. 'I've heard more than enough. Where is this poor man? I must talk to him.'

The farmer knocked out his pipe calmly. 'You have been,' he said, 'for the past half hour. I'd say it looked like rain, wouldn't you?'

Cold enough to...

Sometimes words are superfluous.

I could simply write 'snow' and leave the rest of the column blank and everyone would know exactly what I meant.

Not to mention how I feel, which is miserable. As I watched a group of children sledging, spending as much time in the snow as on the sledge, I tried to force myself to remember how much fun snow could be. It was not easy.

We have just had the eye-popping struggle to get a visiting car up the farm road and another small blizzard was blowing as we tried to spread the right mixture of salt and gravel on the worst patches.

Getting big bales of straw and hay to the cattle was very difficult with the approach strip of concrete more like a skating rink than anything else under the fresh snow. Once inside, conditions were not much better because of the way the wind was blowing the fine, powdery snow which was going straight through the strips of Yorkshire boarding. Added to which my tractor refused to start for what seemed like hours and hours and, in fact, *was* hours.

In all, a liking for snow was further from my mind, yet even after the terrible day we had when I was out late at night checking one more thing I had forgotten during the mental and physical turmoil, the moon was shining from a clear sky on that perfect white blanket. I almost enjoyed the sight.

Almost, but not quite. It was even colder than the night before and I had too many worries about what problems that would give us next day to get carried away. However, I was glad the children had enjoyed it. They have time enough to become as miserable as I am.

Wild Oats and Wellingtons

It could be the blanket of snow will protect us from the worst effects of the frost which is forecast to last for a fortnight. As I mentioned before, I have great trouble recalling the years of notable good and bad expect the ones which everyone remembers such as early 1963 or the winter of 1947. I may be slightly out on my date but I think I remember vicious frosts in early 1978 and 1980, then 1981 but without the cover of snow which makes this seem worse.

The chill factor is something else which has become more widely discussed. It is a convenient shorthand way of stating what we all know too well – that a strong wind makes the day seem longer. On days with a strong easterly wind coming straight from Siberia with not much to stop it, we're in trouble and we should still spare a thought for the Russians and Scandinavians coping with temperatures down to minus sixty.

I am surprised anyone can live at that temperature. I know after a few days of minus five to minus ten I would not like to stand anything much colder. And what do they do about their diesel? The quality of winter grade diesel for tractors and lorries seems to be one of those perennials which produce no satisfactory answer.

Manufacturers insist they have improved the product, but every cold spell produces a crop of complaints. It may be a combination of factors such as diesel quality not being quite what the suppliers claim, and exposed farms with severe chill factors and badly designed fuel systems on some tractors.

A glass bowl perched on the outer limit of the engine does not seem the best place to have a fuel filter. Engineering may not be my strong point, but why an expensive filter which once frozen becomes useles?

I know the old joke about the rich man changing his car because the ashtray was full, it may be time to change our tractor to one with a fuel system which does not seize solid when the temperature drops a few degrees below freezing.

When all things go wrong

Now simply tell us in your own words exactly what happened. Don't rush. Get the facts right.

'Well – it was like this. First thing in the morning several cattle were off colour and scouring. But it wasn't much to worry about. We'd been mucking out the day before and they had been moved into another part of the shed for a few hours.'

So there was no great cause for alarm?

'No, no. As it happened they settled down again during the day. We cut their feeding back a bit and made sure they had plenty of fresh straw to eat.'

That wasn't the problem then?

'Not at all. When we'd finished feeding stock the plan was to cultivate a field ready for drilling with one tractor and put the sprayer on to the other to put liquid fertiliser onto forty-five acres of winter barley. And possibly some of the early wheat. And get the other field drilled in the late afternoon.'

A well organised day ahead.

'It was. Oh, it was. But when we put the crumbler onto the tractor...'

The crumbler?

'It's an implement with two alternate sets of tines and rollers. The tines work through the soil and the rollers leave it firm and level ready for drilling. The front roller is bigger and drives the second roller by means of a chain.'

Like a bicycle chain?

'A bit like that, but enclosed with lots of grease. When we put the crumbler on and gave it a quick spin by hand as usual to make sure everything was okay the front roller spun but the back one didn't.'

And that was when you...?

'No, no. A mere bagatelle. A very small fly in the ointment. We thought the chain had come off, or snapped. What had actually happened was that the key attaching the centre shaft to the outer roller had snapped. A bit more complicated, but only an hour or two's work.'

So...?

'While this was going on I had filled the sprayer saddle tanks with liquid fertiliser, after half an hour or so to get the sprayer on. It takes a while to connect up all the pipes and hoses.'

You were a little tense by then?

'No, fine. But when I filled the tanks as I was saying I realised that the right hand one had a three foot split across the top. Now, by this time Aileen had taken off the crumbler in the workshop for repair and had gone to roll down some ploughing. While Angus and I were discussing

the leaking tank, she reappeared. On foot. Walking.'

She had left the tractor behind in the field?

'Yes. For the very good reason that the front wheels had fallen off.'

Fallen off. My goodness. Ah, so that was when...?

'No, not then either. I may have nodded my head against the mudguard once or twice, but bore up bravely. We assumed it was a simple steering rod break or something like that. Angus went to check while I reckoned I could put the fertiliser on if I only three-quarter filled the tanks. When I came back for the second load, the bad news was that it wasn't a simple steering rod.'

It wasn't?

'No, it wasn't. It was a bloody great...sorry, it was a large repair job. Two brackets hold the front wheels. They're large, but not separate. They don't bolt on. They're an integral part of the whole cast block which weighs about quarter of a ton and costs more than £1,100 new. Not to mention having to take the whole front end apart. And there was still the small problem of getting it in from the field.'

By this time you were tense?

'Are you joking? Show me a metal bar and I could have bitten through it.'

Ah. And that was when...?

'Almost, but not quite. It was starting to snow, turning to sleet. I decided I had to get the fertiliser tanks emptied. I set off up the field. There was this clanging, clonking noise. I'd heard it before. You recognise mechanical breakdowns by the noise they make. The brackets holding the back wheel on had slipped. The wheel was falling off. I drove slowly to the gateway and climbed out and walked back to the steading.'

And that was when?

'That was when this uncalled-for adviser drove up to say there was light leaf spot on the oilseed rape, and where would I like him to put the spray. And I told him the same place I was about to put this fence post I happened to have picked up...'

And every word of the happenings on March 16 at your farm is true?

'Every word. It took us four days, several dozen phone calls, a round trip of 700 miles for a second-hand block, and more than £1,000 to get everything working again.'

Right. Case dismissed. I hope the adviser will soon be walking normally.

Make the most of the worst

Eddie Edwards, the world's worst ski jumper, reminded me of how much fun it is possible to have in snow without laughing.

There is always the chance that the well-known cigar company will then ask you to advertise their antidote to disaster; I've thought of a few possibilities.

Scene: Close up of whistling farmer, wreathed in smiles and steam, as he measures milk powder into two buckets of hot water and begins to mix the morning feed for a few small calves. He stops mixing and tests the temperature and taste appreciatively, not to say daintily, with his finger.

Still whistling and followed closely by the camera he steps out into a world of snow and frost. But not enough snow to make walking a crunchy pleasure. Only enough to cover the hard frost which in turn covers several months of rutted mud.

Whistling, though no longer smiling, the man with two full buckets of hot milk begins to tiptoe tentatively along what he believes to be the best route to the calf pens. In loving detail the camera follows his every move because there is small chance of retakes without nervous break-downs.

His right foot goes one way. His left foot goes another. The buckets are swung frantically in a desperate balancing act. He's going – yes, no, yes. He crashes to the ground in a flurry of violent language. And the wonderful thing about six or seven gallons of milk coming down is that none of it misses him. He gets the full benefit.

As he sits on the frozen ground, dripping with milk and musing on life's rich tapestry, cue for the hand to pocket and cigar to mouth to familiar music. As the milk drips off his cap, still amazingly in place, and freezes down his cheeks the smoke drifts upward.

Scene: A man is loading big round bales on to a trailer with a small tractor and a fore-end loader. He handles it well and skilfully on the snow-covered ground. He is happy in his work, confident in his ability as he slips six bales into place.

Breezily he finishes loading and swings the tractor round to pick up the trailer with the pickup hitch. Anticipation here that this will be the disaster area with the tractor refusing to reverse far enough to pick up the trailer or alternatively sliding teasingly to either side of the hitch.

Instead the operation is completed faultlessly and tractor and trailer set off up the hill. Close up of the driver's change of expression as wheels begin to spin and slip – from half smile as he thinks of breakfast, to the familiar snarl and powdered teeth of the man whose machine is letting him down.

Accepting that he isn't going to make it the driver stops burning rubber and starts to reverse. As the trailer slips sideways into a ditch and bales roll off in slow motion the local riding school comes past in early morning single file of ten curious people.

Cigar smoke begins to drift upwards and the camera doesn't dwell on the fact that the discarded match has set fire to the load of bales.

Scene: A man is trudging through moderately deep snow wrapped in what looks like a random selection from a jumble sale, topped off by a waterproof and a woolly hat.

He is whistling in short bursts interspersed with bawls of what sound like Swahili. In the distance a camera picks up a black and white object travelling swiftly.

Camera cuts back to the man who is now waving both arms and a stick.

Cut back to close up of the black and white object which is a collie apparently enjoying itself in the snow. Suddenly it stops, looks and listens.

Cut to the man who is whistling but has stopped waving his arms and shouting. His day is beginning to improve.

Back to the dog which has obviously received and understood instructions and is starting to move in a purposeful way across the wintry landscape.

Back to the shepherd, for it is he, who has mysteriously become unhinged again. It is clear from the close up view that he has the glazed eyes and hysterical mien of Eddie Edwards about to attempt the 90-metre ski jump. Something has gone wrong.

What has gone wrong is now in camera view – a collie bitch with amorous intentions. The shepherd's dog is heading towards her at a brisk and determined trot with a flock of sheep fading into the distance behind.

The shepherd, screaming in frustration, starts a forlorn race after the dog forgetting last summer's chain harrows hidden in the snow near the gate.

As he lies on his back he reaches for his cigar. Tasteful smoke draws a drifting veil as the two collies meet on the skyline.

The soundtrack fades before a well-placed shot rings out followed by an hysterical laugh. It beats ski jumping.

Exhausting search for truth in the mist of an Irish time warp

'Excuse me, sir, we are doing a survey on people returning from Northern Ireland. Can I ask you a few questions?'

'Mmfh?'

'Would it be easier if I knelt down beside you? Or are you planning to stand up sometime?'

'Yes. As soon as I can find something to cling on to. Thank you. That's better.'

'If a little bit eye-watering. Now was your trip to Northern Ireland business or pleasure?'

'Yes.'

'I see. And how long were you there?'

'About three weeks.'

'According to the ticket you have clamped between your teeth, it was only three days.'

'That doesn't take account of the time warp, Irish hospitality and a schedule of visits which probably contravened the Geneva Convention.'

'You were kept busy?'

'Busy! It was survival of the fittest out there. Only the strongest could stand the pace. Farms, dairies, colleges, research centres, distilleries – they passed in a blur. Particularly the distillery.'

'Did you lose much weight?'

'Lose? I put on twelve pounds. If I hadn't managed to get out before St Patrick's Day I'd have had to buy a new suit. Do you know how many home-made buttered scones, strawberry jam optional, the human body can take?'

'Not exactly.'

'Seventeen. I watched him do it. And that was on top of two airline breakfasts and an Old Bushmills.'

'Old Bushmills?'

'It's an ancient Irish custom. Three of those and you'll believe anything they'll tell you.'

'You mean it's a drug?'

'Something like that. No no not really. It's a whiskey – they spell it with an e you know. It's the national drink instead of tea.'

'Did you like it?'

'We forced ourselves to fit in with the customs of the country. It got easier as the days flew by.'

'Seriously though, was it a working visit? I need to know for my questionnaire.'

'Definitely. Very much so. We never stopped working. Our search for truth made us phone a chief research scientist at two in the morning to check on a story he'd given us that afternoon.'

'Was he helpful?'

'Very. He gave us the most explicit directions we'd had all day.'

'I am still a little confused...'

'Join the club.'

'...about what you were actually doing in Northern Ireland.'

'Finding out about their agriculture. Meeting people. Food tasting. Studying the impact of Spanish-style bunga-lows on the countryside. Doing speed trials in an 18-seater bus on country roads. Climbing hills. Examining fish research work. Visiting a chicken factory. Finding out the difference between a dairy and a distillery.'

'What is the difference?'

'You can walk out of a dairy. Please, don't laugh so loudly. Have we got much further to go? It's not very comfortable sitting on this luggage trolley.'

'I am pushing as fast as I can. It's not usually part of the

22

interview.

'Which bit of the visit did you enjoy most?'

'The farms. I enjoyed that more than anything. Even journalists who'd never been on a farm before enjoyed it once they'd figured out where to put their feet.'

'Why was that?'

'Farmers are much the same wherever you go. They're much happier on their own ground showing you what they're doing, dishing out hospitality. And most Irish farmers are men of regular habits one of which is drinking Old Bushmills.'

'Would you go back?'

'As soon as I've recovered my strength. Is this it?'

'Yes. Wait! That's not a walkway, that's the luggage carousel...Ah, well somebody will lift him off it eventually.'

Load of false hope

At farm sales lots to be sold are itemised as livestock and dead stock.

Dead stock does not mean carcasses. It means machinery, posts, nets, tools and all the other impedimenta of farming.

It is true that it should mean carcasses because livestock do occasionally – all right, frequently – become dead stock. There are many long-suffering expressions in common use to testify to this:

'Aye, where there's stock there's brock.'

'Aye, where there's stock there's trouble.'

'Ah well, these things happen.'

'You've got to have them to lose them.'

No doubt there are many more.

This is only a random sample from those of us who live in the real world and not at long range where losses can be minimised if not entirely hidden between the happening and the reporting.

I read about them in white-hot technological farming magazines. Extreme disappointment while lambing 800 ewes single-handed, each with 2.16 lambs, to lose three lambs.

Suckler herds which average 116 calves per 100 cows, haven't had a dead calf for 10 years or a difficult calving for seven. Calf rearers who have lost one out of 1500.

And so on. You shouldn't really laugh at the people who have convinced themselves that this kind of statistic is true. It's help they need not hysterics.

Put it another way – if no one ever loses animals, why are kennel carts always so full?

Intimations of mortality don't come much more clearly

than kennel carts. For those of you wise enough not to have livestock this is the vehicle which collects nature's little accidents when they become dead stock.

These days it isn't usually a cart at all but a pick-up truck which has the contents open for inspection if you're feeling strong enough. I was about to write 'often enough the load is not too bad', but I wouldn't like to give the impression that we get more visits than anyone else.

What I should say is that on his occasional visits the contents of the truck are not too bad. Casualty animals seem to be reported more quickly these days with those which may have matured beyond reasonable limits buried on the farm.

These limits are fairly elastic. Very little seems to trouble the men who drive kennel carts. Like mortuary attendants and hospital porters there's a spring in their step and a whistle on their lips when dealing with cadavers which the rest of us might envy.

Looked at another way our loss is their gain which may account for the whistling while they work. Personally I don't grudge them it. At a rough count there are 1,706 jobs I would rather do.

Apart from being well filled at any time I have occasion to see one, another reason for my view that any one with livestock gets casualties, is the mileage these pick-ups do.

I had a lift in one recently. Conversation was stilted on my part as I balanced the need to stick my head out of the window at the risk of a bullock's foot in my ear against the unusual atmosphere in the cab.

The driver and his dog didn't seem to mind but there was a certain something in the air which tickled the throat. I opted for the dangers of the bullock foot and shouted over my shoulder.

I suggested that the trucks probably set a record for speed of going through an MOT.

I had visions of seventeen mechanics being put on the job with instructions to get the truck in and out of the garage in about the same time as it takes for a Grand Prix tyre change.

This vision was spoiled by the driver saying that the trucks did so much work collecting dead livestock that they were well over 100,000 miles and worn out before an MOT was needed.

At that point we got to where we were going and I hurt myself in the rush to get out. There's something rather upsetting about the way they call 'See you soon' as they drive away with one more load of someone's fond hopes.

Taking the strain – and the stress – at lambing time

'Oh happy days are here again, the sky is blue and clear again, happy days...'

'You sound very cheerful, dear.'

'Not really. The lambing starts tomorrow. Just packing a few things on my last free day.'

'Lambing! Oh my goodness. I'll pack a few things too.'

'It's all right, I'm managing to get my lambing stuff together...'

'Not for you. For me. I'm leaving home for a month.'

'Now don't be like that. It's not that bad...'

'*You* are. Unbearable. I'm not having another month like last year. I'm going to pack a case. I'm going now.'

'Look, I promise things will be different. I'm much better prepared this year.'

'You say that every year. Goodbye.'

'No, no, this time I mean it. I've got all the individual pens ready for as soon as a ewe lambs. Nearly anyway. One or two to tie together yet. A few boards to nail up...'

'Feed buckets? Drinking bowls?'

'Ah...'

'Iodine? Rubber rings? Milk powder?'

'Ah, let me look, Yes. No. Yes...maybe...'

'I knew it. Disorganised as usual. Goodbye.'

'Wait! You can't go like this. Farmer's wives stick by their husbands through thick and thin. I read that in *Farmers Weekly* homelife section.

'I have done for three lambings. This time I'm going.'

'What about for better or worse?'

'It will be better – for me. And you get worse every year.

27

I simply do not see why watching 400 ewes lamb should turn a reasonably normal man into a raving lunatic.'

'Watching! It's hell out there. You know that. You've done it.'

'With considerably less fuss than you if I remember rightly?'

'Beginners luck. Quietest night we've had for years.'

'Eleven lambed in three hours. And I didn't lose a lamb.'

'I could have done it on one leg.'

'You had to, remember? Breaking your toe by kicking the wall when the ewe moved was one of your better efforts.'

'It was her own fault. Half a shed to herself and one muckle single lamb to look after and she lay on it.'

'Trying to strangle her with the rubber tube on the lamb reviver then kicking the wall didn't help much?'

'I...'

'And what you wrote on her side with the marker aerosol was quite uncalled for when you finally caught her.'

'Well, that's what she was. I'd have written something else if there'd been room. But it won't happen again.'

'I don't care. I'm off. For the duration.'

'Look. Wait. I'll show you. See how well organised I am – lambing ropes...'

'Binder twine...'

'Well, it's close. The vet says a bit of string's just as hygienic to fasten round their legs and pull a difficult one out.'

'Hmm?'

'And look – lubricant gel, plastic gloves, antibiotic, soap, lamb reviver, penicillin, pessaries, colostrum tube, rubber rings – and iodine, I have got iodine, I knew I had a syringe.'

'Stuck, I'll bet.'

'Not at all, look at th...look at th...well, a quick soak in hot water and it'll be fine. Vitamin pills.'

'For you or the lambs?'

'Very funny. For the lambs.'

'And what's in this little bottle? It smells like whisky to me. For the lambs?'

'Some of it.'

'And what's the calculator doing in the lambing aids box?'

'That's to check the actual number of lambs born against the forecast when we had the pregnancy scanner in. It's management control.'

'It's management lunacy. You're bad enough as it is when you count what you've got. If you count what you've lost they'll take you away in a strait jacket.'

'No they won't.'

'Why not?'

'I'll shoot myself first. You're right. Out goes the calculator.'

'Now you're beginning to see sense.'

'I am. I am. I'm sure those yoga classes during the winter are going to help. This year will be different.'

'No more screaming and shouting and throwing sticks at the dog?'

'No.'

'No more walking through the back door without opening it?'

'I'll try not to.'

'No more lying on your back in the mud drumming your wellies on the ground and shouting foot and mouth has a lot to be said for it?'

'Well...'

'I knew it. I've got a better idea. Here.'

'What?'

'You take this case and go away for a month. I'll do the lambing. Where's the box? Thank you. Goodbye.'

Futility of losing one's temper

Many years ago I was given a book by the local minister at a time when he obviously thought there was still hope. It was full of short, morally improving stories about what happened to boys who drank, lied, swore, or otherwise behaved badly.

I think losing your temper figured as well. It was the most boring and most depressing book I've ever read, with the exception of some of D. H. Lawrence's. But if I can find that book I'm going to read it again. I've seen the light.

Mind you I say that every time I lose my temper and have the physical and financial scars to prove it. This time it was a combination of carelessness, bad luck and stupidity. It usually is.

It began when we started drilling spring barley again after a lengthy gap because of rain, although this had had the beneficial effect of softening ploughing which had never seen frost mould all winter and had baked dry and hard in the shrivelling winds.

One pass with the harrows across the ploughing to level out the worst of the humps and hollows was followed by a double pass with the crumbler. The result was the fine, firm level seedbed of the textbooks – in most parts of the field – and nicely, but not stickily, moist to boot.

While Aileen carried on with the crumbling I filled the drill with a dozen bags of Triumph spring barley under a blue sky. A chill March wind negated the sun's heat, but not the mental uplift it gives. There's nothing like the sun on your back in the spring.

Once down the field along the side of the longest, straightest hedge, with the drill clicking and ticking behind as the spring-loaded discs slotted the steady trickle of seed into the ground and the harrows made sure it was safely covered.

I turned at the end and hopped out to lower the second marker, which had to stay up for the first run along the hedge side. Then back into the tractor full, literally, of the joys of spring.

Or almost. A second later I was saying things which would have given the author of that book material for several more improving chapters and the minister scope for a sermon. The stiff breeze had swing the tractor door shut on the end of my middle finger.

Half an inch up or down the door frame would have been rubber beading. Instead, I got the benefit of the door catch.

As the nail turned black before my popping eyes and half an inch of skin and flesh flapped about I took credit for one thing – the small first-aid kit I carry in my bait bag.

I've possibly cut strips of plaster faster, but not often. I had the throbbing digit bound with several layers in less than a minute and carried on.

It was a satisfactory enough afternoon's work eventually, with sixteen acres in, but the small accident took the edge off it. An aching finger attracts bumps and bangs at frequent intervals.

The worst one happened the next morning as the throbbing was showing signs of easing off. I went to start the tractor with the grain drill to move into another field and there was a dull clonking sound.

Although fearing that the starter motor had finally given up, I pretended it was probably a flat battery and tried starting it with jump leads from another tractor. Still the dull clonk.

A severe tapping of the starter motor with a spanner produced no result except several more dull clonks.

It was the next move which caused the problem. I started to remove the useless starter motor. As with the door the day before, a second later I was roaring with pain as the spanner slipped and jammed the damaged finger.

That was when I threw the spanner which bounced off the engine block and shot through the side-window at the front of the cab. Talk about laugh!

The beneficial effect was to calm me down. Losing money always has that effect. We got a replacement starter motor and priced a new window. Twenty years ago we could probably have put down a deposit on a new tractor for the same price.

While we were at it, we priced a new set of foot-long, slightly curved, forged metal teeth for the crumbler. Two years ago they were more than £9 each and expensive. This time they were £16 each and extortionate.

A complete set of new teeth would cost £768. We can do a lot of cutting, welding and adapting for that.

Big Apple faces a porcine plague

Affluent New Yorkers are keeping pigs as pets. Unlike the apocryphal alligators of a few years ago, this latest fad seems to be true, if we believe the photographs.

Remember the alligators? The story was that they were bought at a few inches long as pets. When it became clear that they were growing, a disconcerting habit animals have, they were flushed down the toilet.

In the sewers they grew to an enormous size to terrorise the populace.

If true, it was óbviously terrifying. A spider coming up the waste pipe is one thing, an alligator another.

As far as I remember the story was spoiled, rather unfairly, by not being true. It was in the same category as grandmother dying on holiday in Europe and the caravan with the corpse in being stolen.

Or most of the foreign stories in the Sunday papers. Or possibly the recent story about the Irish cow which lived for several months without water.

But the New Yorker's passion, or to be more accurate, the well-heeled, half-witted New Yorker's passion, for small, pot-bellied Vietnamese porkers seems to be true.

It is only a matter of weeks before we can read effluent for affluent as the black, wrinkly, snub-nosed, five-pound piglet becomes a black, wrinkly, snub-nosed 100lb porker.

It's unfair to say it could only happen in America. Thousands of people in this country have unusual household arrangements to accommodate pets; it's always disconcerting to find that a house is run by something on four legs or that the old joke about 'where does a Great

Dane sleep?' is true.

The answer, on the extreme off-chance that you don't know, is that a 4ft high, 300lb Great Dane sleeps where it likes. Unfortunately, for many pet-owners, the answer also applies to tiny Basenjis and cats.

It will certainly apply to pot-bellied Vietnamese pigs. Pigs are amiable, generally friendly animals, but as a potential household pet they suffer from several disadvantages.

One is smell. The pig has a distinctive, penetrating smell which clings like cigarette smoke or overdone cabbage to its surroundings. If the surroundings are a pig yard, shed or field the smell is tolerable.

But clinging to clothes as it does, the aroma comes back with a rush in a different environment like the village shop or a crowded post office.

I suspect it will be equally penetrating in a New York apartment. Smitten owners have tried to claim that because the pigs have no sweat glands they don't smell.

This is wishful thinking on their part. Their ingenuous claim ignores the basic biological fact that more things smell than sweat.

They appear to think that taking the pig for walkies will solve this problem. It won't, unless they go walkies twenty times a day and carry a large shovel.

Neighbours who dislike what dogs do on sidewalks will be amazed at what a pig can do. Pigs can walk, eat and excrete at the same time and tend to if they're not sleeping.

In a sensible environment this is no problem. In a field it doesn't matter. In a shed, pigs will use a particular part of it. If their chosen spot happens to be the entrance hall of a New York apartment, I suggest the pig-owner has problems.

Telling guests who are gingerly inspecting their shoes that 'it's no worse than chewing gum' won't be an answer.

Neither will shutting doors as the pig gets older, bigger and heavier. Unless the pot-bellied Vietnamese pig is different from every other breed of pig extant, it will chew its way through its surroundings.

Most of them don't do this viciously. They're amiable animals with an insatiable curiosity. They chew something to see what happens. When bits flake or splinter off, they keep chewing. That's why most pig-pen fittings are made of metal or concrete.

True, this eventually erodes over the years because of the high concentration of acid in pig's urine, but it is more chewproof than breakfast bars, chair legs, cushions, and New York apartment doors.

The clincher put forward by New Yorkers paying several thousand dollars for pet pigs – and good luck to the pig farmers who saw them coming – is that Vietnamese pigs have lived with families for centuries.

That may be true. Until not too long ago in this country man, family and animals lived more closely together than now.

In my early days as a reporter I helped clear hens from the kitchen before we got down to doing an interview. In several places the house cow was part of the family. But pigs seldom lived in the house for the good reasons already outlined.

I like pigs – in their place. The only consolation I have is that the Vietnamese pot-bellied pig won't like the arrangement any better than the rapidly-declining number of visitors to New York apartment-owners who are trying to keep them as pets.

But as far as the smell goes it looks as if the pigs will simply have to get used to it.

Living in harmony with our neighbours

As farmers we do have a tendency to shoot ourselves in the foot now and again. And again. And again.

It was something I've noticed before which brought that home to me, namely tractors and farm machinery on main roads particularly over a busy spell like the Easter weekend.

We all know that work never stops on a farm and there's a certain satisfaction in feeling virtuous about working while most of the population seems to be intent on enjoying themselves in traffic jams or rolling dyed eggs in a freezing wind.

And with fertilising, spraying, potato planting and still some grain drilling going on tractors and machinery quite often have to travel along main roads.

We could do it a bit more thoughtfully, particularly as far as grain drills are concerned. Twice last week I saw a tractor pulling a grain drill pull straight out onto a main road, promptly taking up two-thirds of the width.

We all know it takes time to get one of the older grain drills onto a transport trailer, but it makes life easier for everyone if it has to be taken along the road.

Not everyone understands what important work we're doing. It's also worth remembering that farmers are not the most patient of drivers if they happen to get stuck in a jam behind some slow moving vehicle.

It is true of course that some people go out of their way to look for trouble. For some years we were plagued by a couple who moved to the country and bought a house opposite one of our outlying fields.

It was a safe bet that the phone would ring before the tractor which had been working in that field, for whatever reason, got back to the farm to complain about mud, soil or grass on the road outside their house.

Working in the field was like being on Candid Camera. All the time a tractor was working the wife would be at the window or the husband would be dodging about the garden.

It became quite funny, when I was in the mood, to give them a cheery wave or occasionally a V for victory to watch their reaction.

It didn't stop the phone calls, one or two of which were justified and most of which were simply silly. Imagine that you're going to have a pain like that behind you the next time you're on the road with a tractor and think carefully.

Being awkward may simply be farmers fighting back against the rising tide of rubbish which is dumped in the countryside. This may seem vindictive on the part of visitors and holidaymakers until we realise that they dump as much rubbish at their own homes.

Go through a reasonably-sized town now in the early morning and the streets are awash with fast-food wrappers and soft-drink cans.

It's almost as bad as any lay-by you care to mention. We have two alongside the farm and at any given time the bins will be bulging, which is the council's fault admittedly, but they will also be ankle deep in rubbish which no one has attempted to put in a bin.

Some years ago I remember Dick Emery doing a sketch on television where he turned up, dressed like television's idea of a gentleman farmer, at a suburban house.

After trampling a few flowers and making holes in the lawn he tipped a bag of rubbish at the front door and deposited an old mattress on the rose bed.

When the family who owned the house complained he said: 'I didn't think you'd mind. That's what you did to me last Sunday.'

Chance would be a fine thing. But rather pointless because there's nothing we could do with rubbish to make towns and cities much worse. All the talk about educating people to be tidy certainly doesn't seem to have worked.

I'm at a loss to know what to suggest. Farmers are part of the throwaway society too and as long as plastic fertiliser bags festoon fences perhaps we're not in as strong a position as we should be to criticise.

But something must be done and the only suggestion I discount is one I had recently that anyone seen dropping litter in town or country should be shot on the spot, tempting though the idea might be at the time.

Cheers – to what comes naturally

'All right gentlemen. Best of order there, if you please. I now declare this meeting of organic food and drink producers well and truly open.'

'Point of order Mr Chairman. Is this meeting open to conservation grade oatcake producers?'

'Well now, there's been a lot of discussion about the conservation grade product – as opposed to the genuine article.'

'Point of order, Mr Chairman – who's to say what's the genuine article?'

'We are actually. That's what this meeting's all about. It has come to the committee's notice that some of you – no names, no pack drill – are trying to palm off ordinary, chemical laden, produce as organic.'

'Point of ord...'

'Never mind the points of order. Have some of you, or have you not, been growing oats using artificial fertiliser, weed killer and a chemical to kill the mildew and calling them organically produced?'

'Ah, we didn't use much nitrogen fertiliser. Very little weedkiller. Hardly any at all. And if we hadn't put the mildew spray on they'd have died off.'

'That's the point. We're meant to take all these risks. It's part of the fun of being an organic farmer. Don't use artificial fertiliser. Rake out the weeds. Thin crops won't get mildew.'

'Point of order...'

'For goodness sake, what is it now?'

'It's this crate of organic wine that's been sent in for us to sample.'

'Organic wine?'

'Yes, and there's organic champagne, brandy and cider as well – look."

'By jove, he's right. Anyone got a corkscrew? Mmm, very tasty – where did you say it came from?'

'It's what they're going to be drinking at the organic wine fair in Coventry in July. They thought we might like a sample.'

'Very kind of them – don't mind if I do have a top up. Thank you. Now where were we – don't squirt the champagne around like that, it's awfully silly. Ah yes – conservation grade oats.'

'Point of...'

'Will you shut up! One more interruption and I'll take your packet of conservation grade oatcakes and stuff...'

'Mr Chairman – another glassful?'

'Don't mind if I do. Most appealing little number – fine, full bouquet, just a hint of metsulfuron and N35 fertiliser there.'

'No, no, Mr Chairman – it's purely organic. No additives whatsoever.'

'Come, come, pull the other one, it plays God Save the Queen. There's mos' definitely a hint...thanks, jus' a small one if you insist.'

'No, entirely organic. And I'll tell you something else – even if drunk in large quantities it doesn't give you a hangover.'

'Honestly? No, you wouldn't understand that word – I mean sherious...sherious...seriously?'

'So those two that do the muck and magic programme on Channel 4 say. You will not get a hangover.'

'Fancy that! Yes, another little glassful – full I said – wouldn't do me any harm. Oh, show me the way to go home, 'cos I'm tired and I wanna go to bed.'

'Mr Chairman – I must insist. Point of order – conservation grade oatcakes?'

'Oh, put in another way – who cares? Eh? Who really cares? I'll tell youse...you...tell you anyway, who cares – nobody. Do I care? I do not. Oh, how I don't care. Thank you – it's slipping down a treat. Why is the table spinning round like that?'

'This is ridiculous.'

'How dare you! Ridiculous? Never. This is a serious and very nearly sober meeting to discuss organic food, and wine of course. Mustn't forget the wine – thanks, just a large one.'

'Mr Chairman – I didn't even know you drank.'

'Only to excess – look who cares about organic fruit-cakes.'

'Oatcakes.'

'I'm talking about you lot. What I say is, let's concentrate on the organic champagne – oh, all of it gone? Where's the brandy then? All right, the blasted cider – fill that glass with something. Meeting ad-hic-journed...convene at the organic wine fair at Coventry. Cheers. Keep that table on the floor.'

A life with the right direction

You can tell a lot about someone's lifestyle and interests by the way they give directions.

'Past the shop and the post office, turn right by the church, down by the village hall...' suggests a sober, reliable citizen.

'Past the Masons and the Wheatsheaf and if you reach the Queen's Head you've gone too far..' suggests a citizen.

'Up to the Ford garage, right at the next set of pumps, opposite the tyre fitters..' suggests a car owner.

'Down to the tennis club, past the football pitch, right at the rugby ground...' indicates a sportsman.

All right, then, try really hard to see who this is: 'Well, on your left there's a bright yellow field of winter barley, I don't know what he's been doing with it, too much nitrogen scorched it, or not enough spray more likely.

'Okay, if you can tear yourself away from that, you'll soon come to a canny crop of wheat with a big notice board stuck up on the side of the road. I can't remember what it says on the board, but if you look close you'll see he's been running out of seed on the third tramline from the end. You want to turn off the main road just after that field.

'No, no, the turning's easy enough to see. Well, not exactly easy to see, but there's the wheat field I've been telling you about on your right as you turn, and on your left a field of oilseed rape that would break your heart.

'Well, it would break mine if I had it. Pigeons! Thousands of them for weeks on end. Never did a thing about it. Not much anyway. Flapped a few bags about and walked round with a gun once or twice. Not what you'd call serious attempts. Not even a gas gun left on all day, never mind all night.

'Said it wasn't worth bothering about. The oilseed will grow away again, he said. I admit it's growing a bit, but not as much as it should. I mean it should be three feet high by now. Anyway, you can't miss it. It should be full of three foot high oilseed, with a lot of yellow flowers, because it's early this year.

'And it isn't. Isn't full of three foot high stuff I mean. It's stunted, with big bare patches. What? Well if you'd said at the beginning that you didn't know what oilseed rape looked like I wouldn't have bothered explaining it to you. I think there's a sign pointing to Ulgham. That might help.

'If you're still not too sure, have a quick look on your left just before you think you want to turn off. There's a field of gey bare grass, with a few bale shelters and feed troughs, and ewes with mainly twins in it.

'At least they started off mainly twins. He always packs the roadside field like that to crack on he's having a good lambing. He keeps all the singles down on that big park behind the wood. What? No, I forgot, you don't know the area. That's why you're asking directions. I'm getting you there as fast as I can.

'Like I said, they started off as all twins. But he's had at least three dead, to my certain knowledge. When the twins start dying off it doesn't make the lambing average look so clever, does it? Have a bit look as you come up to it – but don't stop the car. Them ewes are getting that little to eat they'll probably burst the fence if they think they're going to get fed.

'Where were we? Don't rush off, you'll lose yourself in five minutes. Less – a minute and a half, that's how long it would take you to miss that roadend I'm telling you about.

'Okay, you've got that turn off sorted out? You'll not get very far before you see the worst bit of drilling you've ever seen in your life. I don't care how much you've seen, this is the worst. I'll guarantee it.

'It's his new tramlining kit. He's had it working the wrong way, at least that's what it looks like – three sets of tramlines, then no tramline. Right across the field. It's better than a play – no, I've not seen that many plays recently, but I usually watch the farming programme. At least I did until they changed it and started making films about trees and the countryside and goats and stuff like that.

'Look out for that field. It'll give you a laugh. When you're past it start looking out on your left for a farm steading that looks like a scrapyard – full of old machinery that should have been hoyed out years ago. He still uses some of it.

'About a mile after that you'll pass some patchy grass fields, probably with cows in. He likes to get them out early and save on the feeding. It poaches the grass all to hell of course, but it's up to him. When you come to the T junction, there's winter beans on the right, and oats just coming through on your left. Ask again at the first farm you come to and they'll put you right for Newcastle. Pleasure – cheers.'

Keeping afloat with a cash flow chart

I usually prepare a cash flow in November for the year ahead. It takes several days to do it properly, but becomes slightly easier with experience.

Like almost every other farming operation I am involved with I would never claim to be an authority. Like the whole middle range of marathon runners I'm keen and do my best, but leave advice and explanations to the specialists.

Having said that I'm continually surprised that more farmers don't do a cash flow. It is laborious, but not complicated, takes time but no special skill, will please your bank manager, and be a big help in running the business.

It is a case of sitting down and working out your likely physical inputs and outputs for the year ahead, then working out what the cost of these will be – and the likely returns.

First rule of cash flow preparation is to be pessimistic about the amount and cost of inputs, and even more pessimistic about probable yields, pigs sold per sow, cattle growth rates, selling price, and anything else.

Even then, prospects will not look too bad. There will appear to be quite a wide margin between costs and returns on the most pessimistic forecast.

The eye-popping comes when the costs which cannot be allocated directly are added up. This includes items like telephone, electricity, machinery repairs and possible renewals, water rates, house rates, bank interest, car running expenses, fencing, drainage, rent, fuel, and insurance.

Oh yes – I almost forgot living expenses.

The second rule is to prepare the cash flow on the basis of what you have managed to do in the past, not on what you would like to do, or tell your friends you do.

Putting in an expected wheat yield of four tonnes an acre will look good, but only until you harvest your usual 55 cwt. Likewise, lambing percentages of 200 when the best you have managed is 154 – or 26 pigs per sow when you average 19.

The list is endless of the way we can fool ourselves. I claim some authority on this because in the past I have toyed with all of them before deciding honesty is the best policy. Like those gravestones which are engraved with 'Not dead, but only sleeping,' we are only kidding ourselves with wildly optimistic forecasts.

This was not intended to be a lecture. My methods may not even be approved by the experts.

All I can claim is that they work: preparing a cash flow and checking it month by month with what is actually happening keeps my nose to the financial grindstone.

It is not easy. It is a human tendency to go and look at good stock before the rubbish, a good field before the bare and yellow one. When you know the view will not be pleasant, you put off going.

In the same way studying the cash flow chart is a pleasure when cheques are coming in and the outlook is good. It is no fun when performance drops below the forecast, or costs are much higher than expected.

That is the time they have to be faced and studied. Here, too, I claim authority as one of the great procrastinators with a wide range of excuses for not facing up to the cash flow like a man.

Lack of time is the most common one. This is particularly true on many of the farms where a cash flow and realistic assessment of the future is needed.

No time because a cow is calving, a field needs drilled, grass needs cut, crops need sprayed, it is silage time or harvest.

Unfortunately, it has to be faced that time spent getting to grips with farm finances is as vital if not more so than physical labour. My rule three of cash flow preparation is to do it yourself.

Get someone to advise if essential or to check the addition – but rub your own nose in all the facts and figures of your business until they are ingrained.

I believe that a sheet of paper with costs and returns you have worked out painstakingly yourself is worth more than a computer print-out by someone else which may be looked at, but not taken in.

We can't get away from it. I believe, and still do to a large extent, that physical performance, good livestock and good crops are important to stay in business.

They are, but it seems to me now that good financial management and moderate physical performance stand a better chance than good physical performance with no thought of the cost.

At least that is my belief. I don't have too many of them, so it may be worth thinking about.

Make it snappy!

Like so many of my ideas, it seemed a good one at the time – take one or two photographs every week as the farming year gently unveiled its mysteries before our wondering eyes.

Then, in years to come, we could pore over a tastefully bound volume of pictures and nod to each other and say: 'Ah yes, I remember when...'

I suppose it's superfluous to say that it didn't work out like that. Not quite.

This had, strangely enough, nothing to do with the quality of the photographs. Modern technology has made the camera almost fool-proof I'm glad to say, and the prints are really quite good.

But there were other problems. Timing was one. The idea of one or two shots each week to give a gradual progression was good in theory, but not in practice.

Not being a real enthusiast the project became like my gardening, that is nothing done for long spells then sudden bursts of activity.

Despite my best intentions several farming operations would go unrecorded before event and inclination would coincide enough for saturation coverage.

I'm grateful to my wife Liz for summing this up objectively while looking through one set of prints fresh from the developers: 'Ah – a tractor and sprayer, filling up. Sprayer with booms in – sprayer with booms out. Sprayer spraying – sprayer not spraying. Driver getting in – driver getting out – driver getting in again. Sprayer going away – going away further – just out of sight – sprayer coming back – at ten yard intervals.'

Put like that it didn't seem quite such a good £3.45 worth

after all. But the problem of being trigger-happy stayed with me.

It was partly because I wasn't confident enough that any particular shot would come out, so took several to be on the safe side. It was also partly because while I was taking them I saw it as an action-packed progression and when developed they all looked much the same.

These are simply amateur photographer's problems. There were others peculiar to farming.

Most critical was the fact that when there is most to photograph, for example at seed time, harvest or lambing, then there is least time to do it.

Try taking a camera with you on a night's lambing. At the end of the night ask yourself what you were most tempted to do with it and it's ten to one that the answer would not be to take a photograph.

Harvest time is not recommended either. There is too much dust, diesel, grease and bad temper, for a sensitive camera lens and a sensitive soul.

In the hustle and bustle, stopping the tractor to unwrap the camera from first its protective plastic sandwich box then its leather case then lining up the shot, takes time.

As the shutter snaps you realise that the combine driver is not waving as a gesture to the camera, but to indicate that his grain tank is bung-full and must be emptied immediately if not sooner.

This is the real problem round a farm. Wandering about with a camera round your neck looking for likely shots is not classified as work.

The result is many photographs of crops, landscapes and animals taken at night when I could walk round with a clear conscience.

The net result is interesting. Now, along with a few others that I've taken over the years, they are not in a bound volume but in a desk drawer. Some day I'll get round to having an exhibition because I'm sure people would be interested in a sprayer spraying – sprayer not spraying – sprayer with booms out – sprayer with booms in...absolutely fascinating.

The man in jeans and worn-out shirt can't really be the farmer

It does happen. Some farm visitors, business or private, have odd notions of what a farmer should look like.

The best was a young estate agent, no doubt fresh from the Royal Agricultural College, Cirencester, who stopped on his way up the farm road as I was braying posts in.

'Excuse me, my man,' he said. 'Is your employer about?'

At first I thought he was joking. Then I measured him up for a summary tap on the head with the 14lb mell I was balancing idly in my hand.

Then I looked at his fresh and eager young face, the hacking jacket, the twills, and the Labrador pup in the back of the car and took pity on him.

If you dress like a sterotype yourself, arrive in what is supposed to be a relatively well-off farming area, and go to see a farmer, no doubt you don't expect to find him in jeans and worn shirt knocking in stabs.

With my free hand I touched my forelock, but resisted the urge to curtsey at the same time.

'Yes sir, he's probably up at the steading giving the grooms and the gardeners their orders.'

I kept a straight face until the end of the sentence, but gave most of the game away by being unable to stop myself adding: 'Ah, that he be.'

The young man flushed, looked at me closely, said 'Thenkyou,' and revved away. A few minutes later he shot past on his downward journey and I touched the forelock again. I think he said something extremely rude.

There have been others since, who don't seem to expect you to be driving a tractor, working with cattle, or carting straw. But he was the best until last week.

We've been painting roofs, an art form peculiar to old buildings with corrugated iron to keep the rain out. They may not look too bad from a distance, but once up there the ground is a long way down, and sitting on the ridge while moving ladders is an experience.

Not a pleasant experience, but an experience. It reminds me of an instrument of torture I once saw in a history book, called a bastinado. That's more or less what I would have called it too.

We were fairly well prepared for the job. The early summer wish to give a steading a new look can send you rushing to the store only to find there is no paint worth using, and a bucketful of brushes which have set solid.

There will be paint, but not necessarily what you're looking for. A selection of tins with a cupful or two in each might produce a pleasant patchwork door, but not much more.

In truth, most of our painting follows Ford's dictum about his cars – any colour, as long as it's black. That means 25 litre drums of bitumastic to cover as much roof as possible.

Putting it on yourself means that the roof gets a decent coating. Some years ago we used a travelling squad to do the job who, we realised afterwards, worked on the principle of paint it fast, paint it thin, take the money and run.

We realised that when it rained that night, and quite a lot of the paint ran into the gutters.

A few years ago, the last time we did it ourselves, spray guns were reckoned to be the best things to use. The problem with them is the amount of rubber tubing and electric cables which have to be trailed around.

I'm not at my best on roofs anyway. The thought of falling is bad enough, but the prospect of being hanged into the bargain put me off spray guns.

Buckets of bitumastic and broad brushes work well enough, best on warm days when the paint flows easily, but not too hot for the fumes and glare to blister the skin.

However, with the best will in the world, when using bitumastic while balancing on ladders, on roofs, not all the paint goes on the surface it is meant to go on.

It goes on boots, rubber gloves and boiler suits, with occasional flicks and splashes on hair and face. The coating gets steadily thicker during the day and for some reason your hair becomes stiff and matted, and stands on end.

It adds up to an unprepossessing look. Which was what our visitor thought.

He arrived as Aileen and I were perched on ladders up the steepest part of the old granary, slapping on paint and working downwards. He called from below to ask if the farmer was about.

Angus was several fields away, digging in a water pipe with the JCB, so I couldn't refer the visitor to him. Rather the worse for paint, I didn't feel like joking this time either.

'Yes,' I said. 'What can I do for you?'

You read about a jaw dropping, but you don't often see it.

'Ah,' he said. 'I see you're busy. I'll call back.'

Not yet he hasn't.

Not quite so tranquil where the action is

There are few finer sights than two men working in perfect physical harmony, adjusting subtly to each other's movements and reacting immediately to every slight change in posture or attitude.

That thought occurred to me the other day when I saw two men steerage hoeing a field of turnips. Steerage hoeing is nothing like perfect harmony, in spite of what it looks like from the road.

From there it's one of those jobs which seem the essence of rural tranquillity. The tractor moves at tortoise speed along the drills where small green turnips sit proudly; behind it the slicing discs and metal feet of the steerage hoe carve either side of four drills at a time while grubbing up the weeds in between.

Out where the action is it's not so tranquil. Many factors, mainly human, interact and mingle.

To begin with, there is the quality of the original drilling. It helps if this is straight. It is easier for the driver of the steerage hoe to follow straight drills than those which weave and bend.

It also helps if the turnips are clearly defined and bigger than the weeds. This is not always possible, particularly if steerage hoeing was neglected during silage or haymaking. If the tractor driver can't see clearly where he is going, or miscounts the number of drills, the steerage hoe may be trying to follow three drills from one set and one from another.

This isn't easy to appreciate until you have tried it. It usually means that no matter how hard the man on the steerage hoe hauls the handles, which is similar to the tiller on a yacht, back and forwards, one part of the hoe, or possibly three, will be ripping out turnips instead of weeds.

This is where the human factors become important. The man on the hoe launches into a litany known and hated by every tractor driver. 'Left a bit – right a bit – left a bit – right – for...'

On the right drills, four of the steerage hoe following four of the original drilling, the old left a bit, right a bit routine will work as the tractor inches in the required direction and the hoe leaves the turnips and gets the weeds.

But on the wrong drills the best efforts of tractor driver and hoe-man may avail nothing. It usually takes a few yards to realise this, by which time both may be apoplectic.

It is made no easier for the tractor driver by trying to steer, which means looking ahead, while glancing behind to see how his partner on the hoe seat is managing.

Strictly speaking he doesn't have to look back, but it reassures the man on the hoe that they're still in contact. Bawling at the back of an apparently deaf head does nothing for morale or good relations.

Even on the right drills, in good going, there can be problems. On hot days, often depending on lifestyle the night before, there is a soporific quality about ticking over gently across twenty or thirty acres.

A man can nod off in these conditions, slumping over the tiller of the hoe like an exhausted mariner, leaving rows of slaughtered turnips in his wake.

Or a tractor driver under glass can become absorbed in harvest prospects, the price of lambs, why the public hates farmers, the result of the 3.30 at Doncaster or whether Scotland can overcome the might of Costa Rica in the World Cup.

Absorbed like this he misses the rising crescendo from behind, which starts politely enough with a request to go left a bit, passes through inquiries about his hearing and general state of health and reaches a climax on parentage and career prospects.

There are ways of overcoming this human factor. One is to steerage hoe on cold and windy days, another is to travel as fast as possible to keep both men, metaphorically on their toes.

It is the same technique a car driver I knew used to waken himself up if nodding off at the wheel at night. He would accelerate then switch his head lights off. I'm not sure what this lunatic tactic did for him, but the effect on passengers was electrifying.

A more common tactic for steerage hoeing, fitting in with a shrinking labour force, is a fixed hoe which puts the onus on the tractor driver to get it right or wrong himself. It may be more skilful, but think of the fun he's missing.

Sad fade-out for farm scene at Ambridge

I'm worried about Phil. I'm also worried about David. Not to mention Ruth, Elizabeth, Sid, Cathy, Linda, Brian, Old Uncle Tom Forrest and all.

In fact, I have mixed feelings about *The Archers*. I can't decide whether this everyday story of country folk is bad or awful, although I should be able to by now – I've been listening long enough.

True, I've generally listened in the hope that it would improve, but I've still listened along with several million others who have nothing better to do.

The fact that I do listen also exposes my double standard because I detest television soaps of any kind, most particularly *Emmerdale*.

My feeble argument for listening to *The Archers* is that you can do something else while listening to the radio, usually driving.

Like many addictions it started innocently enough with the introduction of radio to modern tractors. Before insulated safety cabs the only thing to listen to on a tractor was the roar of the engine, the squeal of machinery and if it was loud enough the sound of your own voice.

Radio changed all that and the change should not be underestimated. It made 10 and 12-hour days on a tractor pass more quickly and provided human contact of a kind for those of us working alone most of the time.

The choice of contact varied. Younger tractor drivers tended to go for Radio One, or the local music station, and older farmers claimed in a crabbie way that they could hear the music long before they heard the tractor engine.

The more discerning among us went for Radio Two in those early days, from Ray Moore for the early starters to Wogan, Jimmy Young when he still did recipes with Raymondo, Ed 'Stewpot' Stewart and 'Diddy' David Hamilton to John Dunne.

In season there were football matches, test match specials on Radio Three and for the mentally unbalanced there was Wimblebore, which usually coincided with carting hay.

There was also, which shows the insidious way these things happen, the news programme *World at One* on Radio Four which I listened to. And trotting right behind it came *The Archers.*

I suppose that like most soaps, or cigarette smoke, it simply grows on you. I'll listen just one more time; I'll only have one more cigarette.

The need to find out exactly what happened when Eddie Grundy left the gate open; the need to have one more puff.

It's a sad state for a grown man to be in and I did my best to break the habit. For some years I managed this intermittently because I wasn't driving a tractor all the time.

From the end of drilling in spring to the start of harvest I could usually do without Ambridge. Also for most of the winter months when I was busy with livestock and the loader tractor did not have a radio.

But come spring, a March day, the grain drill running smoothly behind and at 1.40 pm I would find myself waiting eagerly, if guiltily, for the familiar, tumpty-tumpty-tumpty-tum music and the even more familiar voice of Jill murmuring: 'I'm worried about Phil.'

Or Jack Woolley having a row with his chef Jean Paul or George Barford, the gamekeeper, growling away at Martha in the village shop. Or Jennifer Aldridge, most painful of the whole motley crew, whining about a stain on the carpet or the glue falling out of her fish knives.

It's not easy to admit all this but worse was still to come.

When we expanded and changed our farming policy I began to drive a tractor all the year round.

I could, and did, listen to *The Archers* every day. Not only that, but frequently twice a day, as I reached the terminal stages of addiction – once at 1.40, which is the repeat of the previous night, and again at five past seven for the new episode.

In the past few months I've almost managed to break the habit unless I happen to be in the car at the dangerous time and find my hand straying to the tuning switch on the radio.

But it has been sorry stuff recently, what with Kenton and his antique shop, professional actors pretending to be amateur actors putting on a play, Ruth's unbelievable Geordie accent, Cathy Perks and Sergeant Barry's unhealthy liaison, Gill's bed and breakfast venture, Mrs Perkins going potty, David taking over the dairy herd, and Neil losing his hens.

No wonder I'm worried about Phil. But I'm more worried about the script writers and the agricultural advisor. It's time we got some farming back into Ambridge, got rid of Jennifer Aldridge, choked Linda Snell and pensioned off Joe Grundy. I'm thinking of having a mass protest meeting at The Bull.

Seeing the wood, and the trees

Three years ago this spring we cleared about two acres of former railway line and planted it with trees.

There was quite a lot of work involved. Scrub bushes and brambles had to be cut and hauled out. Existing trees and saplings, almost entirely ash, were cut back and trimmed to leave one straight trunk at every site.

We got some loads of logs, but a lot of debris had to be burned. Then we ran a cultivator along the former track – the rails and sleepers were cannily lifted by British Rail at the time they closed the line – to loosen up the ballast.

We planted more than 600 young trees, a mixture of oak, ash, and sycamore. Each one was inside a protective grow-tube, which gives a miniature greenhouse effect and keeps rabbits at bay.

The tube is fastened to a wooden stake with wire, although in our more recent planting round hedgerows we have used the more convenient plastic slip-on ties.

Comments from other farmers were instructive. They reminded me of the remark by American humourist Will Rogers: 'People say I exaggerate, but I don't. I just watch the government and report the facts.'

One farmer said we were too quick, we should have waited and grants would be bigger.

Another said how good it was to see a farmer doing something positive about tree-planting. Neither then nor since has he done anything himself.

Comments from a villager were almost as helpful. She remarked that we had spoiled her favourite walk by planting it with trees.

Too late, we had planted them. The first farmer has been proved right. Grants have increased. But we haven't lost a lot of sleep over that.

All I want is for the trees to thrive. I calculate that so far about 90% of the original planting are doing that.

They were small trees, particularly the oaks, many less than a foot high. Another 100 – including hornbeam, whitebeam, lime, rowan, horse chestnut, and sweet chestnut – which we planted in an avenue towards the cottages, were about three to four feet high.

We planted these without grow tubes. Only the chestnuts have been savaged by rabbits.

These bigger trees got off to a better start, but the best of the grow-tube ones, much smaller to begin with, are catching them up. Unfortunately, the worst of the grow-tube trees are hardly bigger than they were three years ago.

This is particularly noticeable on the bankings, which are steep. Along the old track, despite the uncongenial ballast and heavy clay soil, almost all the trees are alive, and many are clear of the top of the tubes.

Along the bankings, trees are generally smaller and most of the thirty or so which have died off are on the sides. I think it can only be due to weed, grass, and bramble competition.

They have been weeded each spring, by hand for the worst weeds, and the surrounding area treated with weedkiller granules. But nature, in the form of unwanted plants, doesn't give in easily.

Grass and brambles fight back. Quite a number of tubes have been lifted each spring to remove grass which is growing up the inside and choking out the trees.

I read recently that casualty rates are high among farm-planted trees, up to 50% in some cases. That looks more like a lambing fatality figure to me, but then I'm prejudiced.

In fact, that sort of figure can only be caused by extremely bad luck, or if no attempt is made to control weeds. We've made reasonable efforts to control weeds, and still have casualties, I wouldn't like any more.

The 100 or so planted round the hedgerows last spring to replace felled elms are all alive – so far. As some of these are crabapples, I'm not surprised.

In my experience the less attractive forms of life – plant or animal, with no mention of humans to avoid possible libel – thrive and survive. There can be few less attractive trees than a crabapple, so I have no doubt that the dozen I planted will be around long after the last grow-tube has rotted away.

One snag has become apparent with the hedgerow trees as they clear the tubes. Rabbits can't get at the bottom, but cattle and ponies reach over the fence and chew off the tops. More protection is called for. Or six-foot grow-tubes.

Rabbiting on – on an age-old theme

'Oi! See you Jimmy?'

'Me?'

'Yes, you. Where do you think you're going?'

'Well, I was rather hoping to travel along this crucial corridor between my habitats.'

'You mean you're creeping along my bit of hedge. Would you like a severe bite on one of your protruding parts?'

'Eh, no, not really. I'm just a rabbit going about his business. You know – a bit of nibbling, hopping, tail in the air, what rabbits generally do.'

'I know what rabbits generally do. That's not what I meant. What I want to know is what you're doing hip-hip-hoppitying along this hedge. As chief rat around here, I'm telling you it's private property.'

'Now you see you're making two fundamental errors there. A...'

'Oi! See this?'

'That paw? Ow!'

'Right. No, let's have an answer I can understand.'

'I was only going to say that as a rat you shouldn't really be in the hedge at all at this time of year.'

'It's these mild winters. Instead of moving into the buildings after harvest we decided to stay here. Plenty of fresh air, not so crowded, a hole of your own.'

'Quite. But you're not strictly a hedge-living animal you see. That's probably why you don't understand the vital significance of hedges as wildlife corridors.'

'Cobblers.'

'That too, of course. The other fundamental error is that

the hedge isn't private property as far as us rabbits are concerned. It's a crucial...'

'All right. All right. You've told me that. And I'm telling you that's a load of rubbish.'

'It's what all the experts say.'

'It's what some of the experts say. Not the one that was writing in *The Scotsman* last week. He said wildlife corridors are a lot of rubbish.'

'My, you're well read – for a rat.'

'Thank you. We were talking about hedges.'

'And a good thing they are too. They provide shelter. Keep cows and sheep in.'

'Those big noisy things that trample round the hedgerows and...'

'...yes. Right on your doorstep. I know. They do the same to our burrows. But did you also know that about 20 kinds of butterfly and 100 kinds of moth live on hawthorn hedges?'

'Get away! I've only ever seen tortoiseshells and those little blue ones.'

'That's because you're not a lepi-lopid-lepi – you're not a butterfly expert. And did you know that more than 1,000 different plants, 65 kinds of bird and 1,500 kinds of insects live in hedges? And they're home for half the native mammals in this country as well as being a crucial...'

'What's a mammal?'

'You're not as well read as I thought. I'm a mammal. You're a mammal. Cows and sheep are mammals.'

'Are you trying to tell me we're related?'

'You know what they say. You can choose your friends but you can't choose your relatives...ha-ha. But it's only the smaller ones like us that live under hedges. Dead handy for nipping out and grazing off half an acre of wheat then back in again.'

'I don't go much for grazing. I'm more a heap of grain left on the ground man, or a few of those 65 kinds of birds you were talking about.'

'Ugh!'

'You don't like small birds?'

'I'm a herbivore.'

'I thought there was something odd about all this hip-hip-hoppitying.'

'Must be going anyway. Nice to...'

'Oi!'

'What now?'

'We're back to where we started. Where do you think you're going?'

'I see what you mean. You're not convinced about this crucial corridor between wildlife habitats then?'

'Nutatall. If they were so useful to little furry things like you big furry things would simply wait there to mug you – wouldn't they?'

'Hadn't thought of that I must say.'

'Well, go away and think about it now. And no more hip-hip-hoppitying past my hole, thank you.'

'Okay. But have you ever thought what a pity it is that ecology, once the most admired of the biological sciences, should have become polluted by unscientific baloney?'

'No. But you're obviously very well read – for a rabbit.'

Faith can build henhouses

What is puzzling about the alleged Channel tunnel costing twice as much as it was supposed to and taking twice as long to dig is that people are puzzled.

Anyone who has constructed anything from small henhouse to cathedral could tell the same tale. Take the original cost estimate and double it, then take the estimated completion time and double that. Now you're starting to get close.

It's not hard to see why. If we are thinking of building something new in the first place, we are optimists. An optimist looks on the bright side of time, cost and why he's doing it at all.

Potential problems are minimised or hidden away in that locked box optimists call a brain. On a small scale the idea has to be sold, to yourself or perhaps a partner. On a larger scale perhaps to the bank manager to encourage a loan.

Or in the case of the world's longest rabbit-burrow, it has to be sold to multi-billion loan organisations whose business pragmatism can only be overcome by waving the prospect of earning even more multi-billions before their popping eyes.

It will be clear that to sell an idea to these assorted coves you must have confidence in it yourself. The optimist's first step is pure faith in his own project, emphasising all the advantages from cleaner eggs to better acoustics for the choir to no more queuing for ferries and no more sea sickness and all the while minimising the disadvantages.

Or, better still, ignoring them completely on the grounds that a brainwave has no disadvantages worth talking about. Cost becomes a trifle in the process, a small item which will be recouped immediately if not sooner.

Snags with a henhouse are not terminal. That's why every boy, or those old enough to know better, should try one.

The lessons taught are universal. They start with minor irritations, such as having to go and buy another pound bag of three-inch nails to fasten the second-hand boards together.

This is compensated by being able to drive in shiny silver nails with unmarked heads instead of a collection of rusty ones, forgotten in a tin since the previous joinery project, many of which have to be beaten straight at considerable risk to forefinger and thumb before they can be used again.

A new hand-saw may also be needed because the existing choice lies between an ancient Bushman which insists on cutting an elliptical curve and a six-foot cross-cut last used to saw through railway sleepers with nails in.

Total cost of the henhouse project may well be £45 instead of the budgeted £20. Time taken will be at least double whatever the estimate was because of the time spent going for the new saw, pound of nails, Elastoplast, and the hammer which was thrown at the hens busy scratching up the garden until their new home was ready.

Driving new holes through the corrugated iron used on the roof because none of the old nail holes lined up with the rafters also has to be taken into account.

But it is experience which is cheap at the price, a valuable lesson learned which can be applied to any construction project from then on. Refuse to listen to what the so-called experts say. Take the original cost you first thought of and double it. Do the same with time.

If it is a shed being built to feed cattle in, not that many of those are going up now, the estimated finishing time will be early October, ready for them coming in off grass or from the autumn sales.

The man who has never built his own henhouse, rabbit hutch or fruit-box cartie will believe this estimate. The man who has done these things will not expect to house cattle in that shed that winter. He knows that with luck it may be completed as the cattle should be going out to grass next spring.

There will be delays in delivering the uprights and girders. One load, when it does arrive, will be the wrong size. Roof sheeting will be the wrong length, the wrong colour, or both.

Starting date will be delayed because the previous project is three months behind. If joiners and builders are both needed on site at the same time this will be impossible for five weeks. Co-ordinating joiners, builders, roofers and planners will need a full-time site foreman.

Sir Christopher Wren had the same problems when he built St Paul's. No one told me that. I know.

The cattle shed, or any building, delays can be more smugly borne when you know what they don't, namely that you aren't expecting it to be finished on time and that the real cost has been budgeted not the estimate.

There is another way, which is to build it yourself as with the henhouse. But now estimated completion time has to be trebled to allow for interference from lambing, drilling, harvesting and silage making and original costs still have to be doubled to allow for inflation, unavailable material and stupidity.

Despite the setbacks, the test is whether the construction was worth its double-time and treble-cost. Will the henhouse stay up? Will the Channel tunnel meet in the middle?

Them and us

I don't think we can get away from the fact that farmers are insular. We're happiest when talking to other farmers and are noted for it, even if exactly the same could be said of doctors, dentists, vets, builders or car salesmen.

Our feeling of 'us' and 'them' is encouraged by our specialist magazines and radio and television programmes. If we take them all literally it gives us a very one-sided view of the problems of farming in relation to the problems of the rest of the country or even the world.

One result of this is that we are liable to get a shock when we realise how strongly the rest of the population feels about farmers and how privileged they think we are. Not only that, quite often they simply do not know what we are doing on the farms.

We find this astonishing because the work and the life is so familiar to us. The sight of five tractors in one field, each racing up and down in a cloud of dust with a different implement on in early May makes perfect sense when we know it's someone frantically sowing the last of his spring barley.

To a passing family from the town or city, and there were many thousands of them over the Bank Holiday weekend, the scene might make no sense at all. Fields of winter wheat and winter barley simply look like reasonable grass compared with what ewes and lambs are actually grazing.

They make no distinction between dairy cows and fattening bullocks in a field, far less any distinction between the breeds that farmers get so agitated about.

And the range and cost of the machinery we use is of little interest to them except when we cause minor traffic jams by taking it along busy roads. We know that it is vital to get from one part of the farm to the other to get a job done, they only know it is a blasted nuisance.

And I'm willing to bet that any farmers, or particularly young farmers, caught in the queue would be thinking exactly the same. I always find it quite surprising how my own feelings change depending on whether I'm driving a car on the road or a tractor.

That's human nature for you. Exactly the same can be said of the change in public attitude towards farmers over the past few years.

We've always had a reputation for being insular and for grumbling whether we were doing well or badly.

But until fairly recently we also had the reputation of working quite hard to earn our living and the question of subsidised income did not come up too often.

It did come up sometimes, of course. The jibe about 'feather bedded farmers' made by MP Stanley Evans back in the early 1950s stuck for a long time, and still does.

Evans was referring to the 1947 Agriculture Act which gave the farming industry as a whole confidence and stability to get on with the job of producing more food. This was in direct contrast to what happened after the First World War in 1914-18 when farming was dropped abruptly and slid into the 1930s depression.

This folk memory still lingers, but we forget as usual that the 1930s depression did not just affect farmers. It hit the country and the world and if they were hard times for farmers, they were worse for many millions of others.

The same must be true to some extent now and partly accounts for the way some of the popular press and their millions of readers think of us.

As farmers we read the figures from Common Market negotiations and think that several million tonnes of grain in store, hundreds of thousands of tonnes of beef, milk powder, butter and so on cannot be too bad a thing. It is surely only an insurance against famine and not much to worry about.

If we were on the dole, living in one of the poorer areas of Tyneside or even much closer to home than that, we wouldn't look at it in quite the same way, especially if we were being told by our daily paper how many millions it was costing to store that food and give farmers a fat living.

Naturally, we don't see it that way and that seems to be the whole problem. Farmers tend to have a blinkered view in one direction and increasingly the public at large have an equally blinkered view in the other.

I don't think there is much point in the amount of talking which is going on just now about 'improving farming's image' until farmers themselves make some effort to understand why the public don't like us as much as they used to.

Something to beef about

Farmers' self-defence campaigns have never been particularly successful. A few years ago, for example, they tried to respond to attacks with the slogan 'Don't criticise farmers with your mouth full'.

Trying to point out that they supply about three-quarters of the food eaten in this country didn't catch on, any more than the robust, if misguided, slogan of farmers in Hereford who tried to reverse the change in our eating habits with a car-sticker promotion which urged 'Eat more meat you sods'.

In the past few weeks they could have had most of the nation's food writers in mind. The thing about being well-fed, not thirsty, and well-paid for writing about food, seems to be that it makes you extremely choosy.

A frenzy of food writers and columnists have put the boot into farming harder than ever in the past few weeks because of Bovine Spongiform Encephalopathy.

It's not hard to see why. The word 'farmer' has been enough in recent years to trigger-off criticism. Add the words 'animal disease' and it's enough to have any self-respecting columnist, or even Jack Maclean, foaming at the mouth.

Never mind smoking, drinking and traffic as a source of death and destruction. Never mind muggings, violent crime or murder. Never mind that the millions starving in what we used to call The Third World, but now called under-developed countries, would eat as much beef as anyone cared to give them.

Never mind that it's less than forty years since food was rationed in this country. Never mind that it's less than fifty since large areas of Europe would eat dog, cat and rat if they could get it.

Never mind that lack of food of any kind is precisely what threatens the Soviet Union now. Never mind that millions of people in this country would be extremely glad to have as much to live on for a week as food writers get for one article urging them to eschew 'unnatural' food and eat only what is 'fresh natural and preferably organically produced'.

No, farmers did not simply make a mistake in thinking that processed animal remains in meat and bone meal – the same material that 13 million gardeners use on their roses – would be a useful source of protein.

No, it was part of a deliberate plot to produce animal products as cheaply as possible while infecting or poisoning the population.

It's come home to roost now of course, if that isn't too much of a metaphor reminding us of the last scare on salmonella, not to mention listeria. As we all know both these scares were caused by rapacious farmers and had nothing to do with careless preparation and cooking.

The faith of the food writers in anything not produced by British farmers is almost as touching as that of county councils.

British farmers are accused of greed and perfidy for producing as much as they can as economically as possible. Industrialists collect Queen's Awards for doing the same thing, but never mind.

Greed and perfidy does not of course apply to any farmer who is not British or who claims to be producing organic food. If the French say they are producing organic chickens then so they are.

If the French, Dutch and Germans say they have no cases of BSE then certainly they don't. Believing in all countries but their own is a perverse reverse xenophobia; maintaining that all food must be organic, or at least produced without artificial aid of any kind, is the kind of snootiness that comes from having a large disposable income. This holier-than-thou attitude is depressing. We know farmers and the food industry have made mistakes. Haven't we all? Haven't food writers?

But farming's biggest mistake has been to adapt to changing times while trying to make a living.

If farmers had had the sense to stay as they were, in the days of outside toilets, once-a-week baths, sheep eaten alive by maggots, winter milk which tasted of turnips, fly-blown meat, blighted potatoes, food crops sprayed with arsenic, and why not salt beef in barrels with weevils for company, none of this criticism would have come their way.

Free-range hens on the midden, pigs kept in the same shed as fattening cattle to live on the grain which passed through in their dung, milk which spread tuberculosis; it's a great pity the good old days have gone.

Instead we have shops, from village to supermarket, which offer good-quality, well-presented, reasonably cheap food.

It is little good farmers pointing this out, or that they have a good safety record notwithstanding scares and salmonella, listeria, BSE and whatever the next one happens to be.

A few scientists and a lot of food writers have convinced millions that a forkful of British-produced food is as safe as prodding a hand grenade.

Well done. All we need to know from them now is precisely what is left on the menu, from which countries, and how much it will cost. And where one million people involved in the British food industry can shoot themselves without being too much of a nuisance.

Entering into the spirit

'Now you're not going to be miserable this year, are you?'

'Me? Miserable? At the Highland Show? Never!'

'You will be when I tell you you're not going near the bar.'

'What! Oh – my arthritis. My gimpy leg. I'll have to sit down. That's a good spot over there.'

'No. That's a bar.'

'It's just a wee bar.'

'No. This time we're going to see the show. I'm fed up with coming here every year and you disappearing half-way round the flower show.'

'But I come back.'

'Yes, about six o'clock stotting.'

'I meet so many old friends. It's just a dram for old times' sake. I manage to get round all the trade stands I want to see.'

'You mean all the ones that hand out free drinks to boost trade.'

'That's very unkind about a public spirited group of men. That's what oils the wheels of commerce at this show.'

'It's certainly what oils you. No – don't move. We're going to take an intelligent interest in the show this year. I've got a catalogue. Now where are we...?'

'Well, the Herdsmen's Bar's over there and...'

'Stop! Here's what I'm looking for – I'm very keen to see this...'

'Not the flower show – not the WRI – not the forestry...'

'No, it's a history lesson to treasure. "A unique exhibit tracing 5000 years of agriculture".'

'Good heavens! That's nearly as long as Ian Morrison's been writing about it.'

76

'Don't be silly, please. It traces farming history from earliest times up to the Second World War...'

'That's when they needed us. That's when this country realised how important farmers were. We showed them how to do it...'

'You were six at the time.'

'Ah, but...I was doing as much work as a full-time man. Born to it, you know, work twelve hour days on a plate of scones and a pickle milk.'

'It takes more than that to keep you going now.'

'Speaking of which...'

'No drink! Now isn't this interesting?'

'I've got better stock than this at home.'

'So I should hope – that one's stuffed.'

'Sorry – force of habit saying that. Come on – this is all very interesting, but let's get out and see some action.'

'I've told you...'

'No, no, I mean the livestock judging. You can't have a better advertisement for Scottish farming than the livestock at this show. Except mine, of course, if I'd had time to get them ready.'

'What a blether you are. You're right though – there's a lot of good stock in those rings.'

'With the sun shining it nearly takes your mind off things. All these farmers going about as if they hadn't a care in the world. Some of them even look as if they're enjoying themselves.'

'There's no law against it.'

'I know, but you'd think some of them would have the grace to look worried. See that chap over there – the one with the green bunnet...'

'About twenty men over there have green bunnets.'

'All right, with the shooting stick then – he's in a bad way, they say. Lucky if he gets through to harvest before the For Sale signs go up. Ah, a bad go. And him over there – the one following the dolly bird – the bank is ready to foreclose any day now...'

'Stop being such a misery. I thought this was supposed to be British Food and Farming Year, cause for celebration, our wonderful farmers, and all that?'

'So it is, But facts are chiels that winna ding – or dong come to that – farming's in a bad way, there's no doubt about that.'

'Then why all the celebrating and publicity?'

'A brave smile on the face of a dying man. We're going down with the ship. It's like rearranging deck chairs on the *Titanic*. Fiddling while Number 10 burns.'

'Mixing your metaphors aren't you?'

'No, just wishful thinking. I suppose we'll get by, but it's hard going. This show's doing its best to be cheerful, but mark my words, it's a struggle.'

'For goodness sake, cheer up. You're a representative of Britain's biggest and most essential industry, producing

75% of the food we eat.'

    'You're a fund of information.'

    'I'm reading the leaflet here.'

    'Ah, Eck – grand to see you. I'm just off to do my chores.'

    'What chores?'

    'Thanks, I'll have a dram. See you later, dear.'

Wishing you'd never started

We had a bullock chewing a piece of string the other day. Not a short piece, but several feet long which had come off a round bale and been trampled almost into the straw.

Not quite trampled in, unfortunately, because the bullock found it and started chewing and swallowing. When we got it, it had reached the stage of wishing it could stop chewing, but couldn't get rid of what it had already swallowed.

As is the way with animals you try to help, it set off round the pen at a gallop, but we finally managed to corner it, grab the string and haul it out.

There are more pleasant things to haul on than several feet of slaver-covered plastic twine, but eventually the last of it appeared and we all felt better.

Two things occurred to me as the bullock stotted away to get as far from us as possible. I remember them particularly because thinking of two things at the same time means I must be having a good day.

One was that no matter how hard you try some bale twine will always end up among the straw. Goodness knows we try hard enough to cut cleanly and remove every piece, but there's always a little that slips through.

Usually it isn't found until we're spreading the midden. Then it will be spotted dangling from the muck fork or appear wrapped round the flails on the spreader.

If there's enough of it, by which I mean far too much, it will eventually wrap up a flail completely and there's the good clean fun of clambering in to the slobber with a Stanley knife to slice it all off while avoiding doing the same to a finger.

Although there's always some no matter how hard we try

I have to say that by far the untidiest midden anyone will ever spread – I don't care who and I don't care where – will be that from stables.

I don't know what it is about these places. The horses are well cared for, but the amount of string and rubbish which ends up in the midden is unbelievable. I think they simply cut the strings and leave them where they lie.

Either that or they carefully collect them from among the horses' feet then throw them in the midden with the straw. Perhaps they think the twine is biodegradable.

It certainly isn't, as anyone who has tried to spread a stables midden will testify, probably at length and using bad language.

Over the years I've been involved with spreading middens from four stables, at a steadily escalating fee, and there wasn't one to mend another.

Once the string, plastic bags, bits of wood and a few lengths of metal pipe had been removed from the last one, I estimate that about half the midden was muck to spread.

The string seems to have reminded me of more than one thing. But the second main thing I was reminded of as we separated the bullock from his unwanted stomach contents was creosoting.

If the link seems tortuous it was simply that the bullock had reached the stage of wishing he hadn't started, but was unable to stop. I'd reached that stage with the creosote and the Yorkshire boarding on the big shed.

It was some time since it had been done. Rephrasing that, it hadn't been done since the shed was built some years ago and I realised that for at least three years I had said every summer: 'A coat of creosote wouldn't do that boarding any harm.'

And that was as far as it had got. Until this year when I took the decisive step of buying the creosote and a brush and setting to.

One side had to be up and down the ladder work and if you don't think that's tiring, try it. As with many other things if I'd been twenty years younger and three stones lighter it would not have been much trouble.

As it was, it was. I persevered, but at night found the back of my legs aching and my toes curling prehensilely in my slippers.

The other side was much more straightforward. We could get the forklift in with a strong pallet on the forks to provide a firm platform. We rattled along that side in good style.

Both ends brought a new problem. At a certain height I get vertigo and go weak at the knees. Unfortunately, there is no precise guide to this height.

At one level I'm fine. Two inches higher and I'm clutching the floor and trying not to pray. We solved the problem by changing places, with me driving the forklift and the former driver creosoting the peaks of the pointed ends.

It was worth it in the long run, but on long stretches of endless Yorkshire boarding I had every sympathy with the bullock.

There's no business like show business

Now for something completely different – harvest.

Only joking. Things are going so wonderfully well this year that it gives me time to concentrate on my plans for the complete reorganisation of agricultural shows.

There are a lot of them about at this time of year and to the layman one looks much like another. Last week I put forward my ideas for revolutionising main ring entertainment with, for example, combines emptying grain into trailers at full speed across foot deep tramlines.

Now I am grateful to Beadnell Village Hall committee for the second stage of the masterplan. It's one of those stunningly simple ideas I wish I had thought of but, as an elderly relative remarked, no doubt I will.

The Beadnell idea is to have an Alternative Produce show before the main Flower Show season begins. There are many more flower shows than agricultural shows although they are even more much of a muchness. But what do I know.

The alternative produce show would have classes for the biggest weed or the most misshappen potato. There will be a section for the poorest pot plant and the worst floral arrangement.

The industrial section – a confusing name for those who don't go to flower shows, meaning as it does baking, sewing, knitting and jam making – is not forgotten. Entries will be accepted for the heaviest scone or the worst sponge cake.

The beauty of the idea is devastating. It throws open the showring to a whole new group, a substantial one at that, of competitors. The fact that judges will be selected who know nothing about the section they are judging is not such an innovation, more an extension of an existing trend.

Starting with livestock as opposed to horses there are endless possibilities for the Alternative Agricultural Show. Take any breed of sheep and have a class for the worst ewe which failed to rear a lamb in the past year.

Another class could be for ewes which should have had twins but hung one at birth and lay on the other. A special class for those ewes which managed to dispose of triplets would carry with it, for the winner, a year's subscription to the RSPCA.

The ewe lamb with the worst undershot jaw would be a prize worth winning. Likewise the ram lamb with the poorest reproductive equipment or the worst case of foot rot.

There would be prizes for the most obvious cases of flour-whitening on fleeces or black boot polish on sheep's feet.

Entries instead of being the usual handful in each class would swell to several hundred.

Judges would have a genuine reason for taking an hour to judge each class instead of footering about inspecting the same three from twenty different angles.

In the similarly crowded cattle lines the same criteria would apply. There would be an award for the cow with the worst udder, the bull with the worst conformation, the stockman who looked least like the animal he was leading.

Instead of classes for a single steer with not more than two broad teeth – a technical expression indicating age – there could be a class for very old cattle with no teeth at all.

There would be a class for cows which should have been in calf, but aren't; a class for bulls with the lowest weight gain from the most amount of food; the most excitable bull of any Continental breed exhibited entirely without tranquillisers and towing a lorry.

Instead of butcher's classes for prime lamb and beef cattle there would be a grader's reject section. Judges, then the public, would be asked to spot the difference.

In the horse lines, now a mainstay of most agricultural shows, the choice would be embarrassing. A class for the most badly behaved pony could be held in close conjunction with one for the most badly behaved rider; competition would be keen anywhere.

Instead of, for example, 'two or three year old filly or gelding to exceed 13 hands high, unlikely to exceed 15 h.h. at maturity, likely to make quality working hunter pony' we could have the much more accurate 'filly/gelding, uncertain age, over 13 h.h. when prodded, most unlikely to reach maturity, certain to be inferior quality if it does'.

There would be the usual snorting, prancing and cavorting in front of the judges, only at the alternative show the exhibitors would be left to get on with this themselves while the horses could stand and watch.

The beauty of the scheme would be the extra entry money and enthusiastic participation. And everyone could say, in perfect truth for a change, that they had better ones at home.

Down to earth with a bump

A Rolls-Royce negotiated the farm road the other day. As I knew I hadn't ordered one recently I was agog to discover whether Royalty had taken a wrong turning or whether Berwick's mayor and sheriff had gone upmarket.

Nothing so exciting. They were simply looking for a flat grass field to land helicopters; something to do with the Game Fair at Kelso at the end of July which is being forecast to break all records.

We chatted of this and that for a few minutes then the Roller and its passengers glided off to check other possible sites nearer a main road.

There was a sense of *deja vu* about the episode, that feeling that I had been through this before but for the life of me I couldn't think what it was immediately.

Watching a Rolls fade into the distance is not an everyday happening and any other connection, for example between it and my own car, could only be coincidental in that both had four wheels.

It came to me eventually because I worry about these things. It was the advertising agency which wanted to make a film on the premises some years ago. They had a Rolls Royce.

The phone rang at the civilised hour of lunchtime. The voice was equally civilised: 'Ah, good afternoon, sir, we understand you have a farm.'

Anyone who calls me sir is off to a good start even though it is almost certain that this expression of deep respect will be followed by a request for a favour. I gave a cautious yes that we did have a farm, but as tenants we were in no position to sell it. It was that sort of voice.

'No, no,' it chuckled, 'we're the highly respected advertising agency for a highly respected motor car. We think your estate might make a good background for an advert.'

'Sir' and 'estate' were getting to me. I know a man who describes a big old house and four acres of rough grazing as his Borders estate, but we had never gone in for such description ourselves. This was an interesting phone call.

'We believe,' went on this persuasive voice,' that you have a hill.'

I was inclined to say that if we only had one hill we would be happy. Life seems to be one long round of navigating their ups and downs. But I restrained the remark to fit in with the general gravity of the conversation.

'Yes,' I intoned, 'I think we may have a suitable hill for you.'

'We also believe that you have cattle,' went on the respected advertising agency as if it was rather a nasty thing to do. With prices as they were then it wasn't a sensible thing to do, but there was nothing particularly nasty about it.

I could only surmise that the caller may have had an unpleasant experience with cattle and one of his cars. He didn't sound like the sort of man who was well up on mart prices.

'Yes,' I said. 'We have cattle.'

I had realised by now that he was working through some kind of check list of questions like an amateur chat show host so was not taken aback when he asked next: 'Are they Continental cattle?'

'They could be,' I replied cautiously, reasoning that in the soft-focus shooting of an advert a bunch of Friesians in the background would serve the same purpose as a bunch of Charolais or Simmentals.

'And have you a pine tree?'

I paused. A bunch of cattle by any other name might get by but the voice on the phone could probably spot the difference between a dying elm and a majestic pine.

'Er...are you thinking of paying for a background for this

advert.'

The voice chuckled again and mentioned a figure which would give us a good start in setting up a suckler herd.

'Yes,' I said briskly, 'we have a pine tree.' I knew where one could be dug up and transplanted, no doubt at a modest cost.

'Fine,' said the voice – it had a name like Giles or Lochinvar but I forgot the details at the thought of money – 'may we come and visit your estate to assess suitability?'

We fixed a time and day and I planned to be resplendent in twill and tweed when they arrived. It was unfortunate that we got involved with moving recalcitrant pigs and I was actually resplendent in sweat and slobber when we heard the soft hiss of the car during a lull in the squealing.

It wouldn't have mattered. These were men of instant decision when it came to assessing suitable backgrounds for their expensive cars.

In the ten seconds it took me to reach the front yard their car had purred into reverse, spun neatly and was heading down the farm road. A pity; it had been quite a struggle moving that pine.

The trouble with rabbits

I don't know how general it is but the rabbit population has increased dramatically in our immediate area.

It is a bit depressing after the concentrated efforts we made over the winter to get rid of as many breeding adults as possible to see dozens of half grown ones bobbing about now.

That is no exaggeration. I was tempted to write 'hundreds' but managed to restrain myself. Dozens is bad enough as they stick their white scuds in the air and hop off the headrigs into burrows in the banking.

Shooting them provides some sport if you are keen on that sort of thing and a reasonable shot. I'm not really either.

The pleasures of ferreting are something else which escape me although we have had our share of helpers with them.

Expectations seem to vary. We had one group of three who set off with ferrets for a day along the banking and came back tired but apparently happy with a total bag of eight rabbits.

We have a much more professional type who works alone for an hour or two and reckons to kill at least a dozen before he thinks it worthwhile which I would have thought was more like it.

But both these efforts still come under the category of sport and relaxation rather than a concentrated attempt at eradication to reduce grass and crop losses.

That has to be by gassing during the winter which was what I conscientiously tried to do. The number of burrows re-opened in the worst areas dwindled each time and I honestly thought they had been severely affected.

It doesn't seem like it judging by the numbers of young. All I can think is that it would have been much worse if nothing had been done although I suppose there must be a limit to a rabbit population in any given area, dictated by the amount of food available.

There is going to be nothing else for it but another full campaign against them this winter or the employment on contract of a rabbit catcher.

When the government withdrew grants to the rabbit clearance societies some years ago there was an immediate and rapid drop in membership and almost all closed down – one more example of our unwillingness to help ourselves.

The results of no organised rabbit clearance scheme and the apparent waning of the effects of myxamatosis disease are now apparent – thousands of rabbits throughout the area all eating their heads off.

Their effect on some fields can be devastating with up to fifteen acres reported as being eaten off completely.

Looked at half-humorously that could be the rabbit's contribution to the grain surplus problem. If there was some way the money from the lost acres could be recouped in sales of rabbit meat it might not be such a bad thing.

As it is, bare headrigs and patches near the headrigs eaten out completely are on the list of minor disasters which cause hair pulling and stifled screaming at this time of years.

Pigeons on later drilled crops of peas are another and it won't be long before the crows start on the more forward winter barley as it reaches the attractive milky-ripe stage.

Lambs are also at that stage where their activities away from their home field become more noticeable.

It must be rather like the development of limbo dancers or contortionists that the younger they start the more supple and proficient they become.

If a lamb starts creeping under or through a fence when small it seems able to get through the same gap months later when it has doubled or trebled in size.

Finding the gap when three quarters grown it would make nothing of it; having come to know and enjoy the sense of freedom it zips through disregarding the laws of space and proportion.

And from being half-amused at the antics of small lambs going through a fence it becomes exasperating as they get older. The moral is always to have the fence stock-proof from the first and some of us find this easier to achieve than others.

A wandering ewe of course is enough to drive the most placid of us demented and few farmers can be described as that.

I remember a comment in one of the farming papers some years ago that the only place for a horse was somebody else's farm or a Belgian deep freeze.

The same applies to a wandering ewe except that she already is on someone else's farm and they don't want her either.

Facing a long wait in the war against wild oats

One of the illusions I've shed over the years is that wild oats will be eradicated before I'm too humpy-backed to carry a bag of them. Each year I win the battle, but the war threatens to go on for a long time yet.

In fact I've never allowed myself many illusions – a naturally broad cynical streak, being brought up on a working farm and dealing with breed societies and NFU headquarters at an impressionable age saw to that.

I did have an idea that in ten years we could get rid of wild oats, particularly as only three fields were badly affected, another three or four had modest wild oat populations and the rest either had only a few or were clear.

Time, as it does, seems to have galloped as far as the wild oat control programme is concerned. Conscientious roguing each year plus spraying for the worst-affected fields has made a big difference – but with only one year of the self-imposed eradication programme to go I've already admitted defeat.

So this is the tenth year we've tramped the fields, plastic bag firmly clutched, ready to pop in wild oats before they escape or if things get too bad, to pull over our heads.

There's been the misery of going into a field thinking that it had been virtually clear the year before only to find a wild oat explosion had taken place. There's also the occasional reverse happening of going into a field expected to be bad and finding it almost clear.

Most of all there is simply the walking up and down, up and down. As virtually all our fields are on hillsides there always seems to be more up than down except occasionally when we drill across the hill face.

I've always intended to buy a pedometer to strap to my leg to find out just how far I walk on an average roguing day. Knowing field lengths gives a reasonable estimate, but it would be nice to know exactly then I could work out how many yards to the wild oat.

In reasonable going – that is, good to firm underfoot and unencumbered by leggings, wellingtons, hats or bulging sacks – I reckon a steady pace of about two miles an hour is my travelling speed.

To a non-roguer this may not seem fast, but consider that much of it is uphill and there are occasional pauses to pull a wild oat.

There are also days of high humidity, beating sun or rain, howling gales and the insect hordes which are attracted to steaming skin.

All this is made partially worthwhile by the fact that all fields now have less wild oats than they did and that several are completely clear; but this is complicated by several factors. There is nothing scientific about what follows, it is simply my own impression of this particular job.

First, the change in our cropping pattern. Nine years ago we grew mainly spring barley with some wheat, now we grow roughly equal quantities of winter wheat, winter barley, spring barley and oilseed rape and peas.

The autumn drilled crops do not give the spring-germinating wild oats their chance to establish. Wild oats in winter wheat and winter barley will almost invariably be found, if there are any, on bare patches or by the side of tramlines.

From my own records there is no doubt about this. Over a range of fields, if there were an average of fifty wild oats an acre in spring barley the average in wheat or winter barley will be less than ten.

In one particular field, its last spring barley crop had more than ninety wild oats per acre. Under wheat it had two. This year under winter barley I found none at all; but

I expect to when it goes into spring barley, whenever that is.

Again for those without wild oats who may be anxious to cast the first stone, fifty to a hundred wild oats an acre may seem a lot. In fact that level of infestation would not be really noticeable.

If a field looks badly infested you can be certain that a wild oat count would be one thousand per acre and upwards. You couldn't count individual oats, as we do, but simply by the bagful.

Second, of course, the weather. A wet year seems to produce an increase in numbers. As this summer has been very dry with us I can't read too much into the generally low numbers we have found.

Third, the quality of roguer. For two or three years I tramped the fields with a squad of youngsters. Their attention waned as the day wore on and having to spend so much time making sure they weren't missing much I began to miss wild oats myself.

The idea of numbers and speed was good in theory but in practice we find that one or two of us working steadily get better results.

Fourthly, there is commitment which the youngsters lacked and for which I do not blame them at all. If they weren't our crops I'm roguing I would have trouble with my own commitment as the days go by and wild oat images flicker on the wallpaper.

Now, like the Russians when the first ten-year plan doesn't work I'm going to give it another go with another plan. Every field clear by 1997 – I can hardly wait.

Ungrateful beasts

Down by the riverside is fine in the song, but not so good on a humid summer morning trying to corral and dose a bunch of cattle who think they are whippet cross kangaroos.

If cattle could reason, the sight of what they were going to be dosed with might have something to do with the extra spring in their step.

As they couldn't have a clue what the boluses in the box were, each one about the size of a packet of mints with the hole, their behaviour could only be explained as natural awkwardness.

The riverside haugh is theoretically about twenty acres in a long, narrow strip of humps and hollows. Move one was to get the twenty-three big cattle off this into a small paddock.

Move two was to get them off the haugh into the small paddock after they charged straight down it the first time, smashed a rail and cleared the fence.

Luckily, half a dozen refused. This would have been four faults in a show jumping competition, but earned our gratitude. Instead of charging into the distance, those which had cleared the fence turned round to find out why the rest weren't following.

This gave us a chance to rally our forces, namely Angus and Alan, to get behind them and me to guard the fence, and bring them round again.

Once into the paddock they were coaxed into a temporary corral of stout posts and gates with a six-foot wall along one side and a wooden shed along another. A bale of fresh hay helped, although they probably chewed away at this more out of curiosity than necessity.

The trick then was to get them into the cattle crush one at a time, slam the door behind them, secure their head in the adjustable gate and administer the long-acting bolus.

Each bolus contains six separate doses of chemical which are released automatically at three weekly intervals to kill stomach worms. A metal slug at one end keeps the bolus in the animal's stomach to carry on the good work.

They are expensive, at £8.50, but should mean that the

riverside rodeo will only be necessary once all summer. I was going to add 'how I hope so,' but with one or two exceptions the operation went remarkably well.

One exception was the jumping ability of these cattle. A five-bar metal gate was no obstacle. One-and-a-half still didn't deter one which rose vertically and clung precariously for a second or two before crashing back to try again.

Trying to get the real troublemakers into the crush first was not a success. They twisted, turned, and spun round so much that they agitated even the relatively quiet ones waiting their turn.

The result was, as usual, that the worst were left until last. The last resort was to leave the exit gate of the crush open as well as the entrance. As the bullock entered in the belief that the way was clear, the trick was to slam both gates at once.

The snag was that the bullock entered the crush at a gallop instead of a cautious walk. Getting the exit gate closed in time to stop it became a fraught manoeuvre.

Angus succeeded, but it was a close thing. Getting the back one shut was also a narrow squeak. As the front gate slammed in its face, the bullock hit reverse and the back gate jammed.

There followed a brief, but animated struggle between me and the bullock's back end to get the door shut. I did, but the bullock had the bovine equivalent of the last word.

This seemed to attract more midges to me than ever which, considering that there were several million of them to start with, hardly seemed possible.

A river on one side and woodland on the other, combined with sweating cattle and humans in a small airless space, seemed to be a lethal mixture. It was hard to breathe without sucking in midges.

Keeping as much of the body covered as possible meant sweating even more. Taking anything off gave the midges an excellent target.

Small wonder the cattle wade out into the water occasionally or find themselves on the wrong side of the fence as they follow the breeze which keeps them clear of insect life. I hope they appreciate our efforts to keep them worm-free.

Advice straight from Never-Never Land

'Hello there, you must be Jack.'

'Yes, but...'

'Giles Cholmondeley, management consultant.'

'Chol...'

'Pronounced Chumley, you know.'

'Chummy...'

'No, Chumley, but never mind. Call me Giles – farm management consultant. SOP PDQ – that's our motto.'

'S...'

'Sort out problems, pretty damn quick. Now, about your problems...'

'Look, Chummey, I don't have any...'

'Oh, nonsense. Everyone has problems. Look, I'm dictating them into this little hooha here then I'll print them out on the portable computer for you.'

'But I didn't...'

'...get my letter? Must be the post. Said I'd be here at 9.0 a.m. prompt and here I am.'

'But I don't...'

'Yes, you do, Jack. That's the mistake all you farmers make. You don't need us, you say. But you do. You really do. Right. There. Five minutes and I've summed up your problems. The cow has to go.'

'What – Buttercup? Go? Where?'

'She has to go. She's uneconomic. And you need the money. See the printout? It all makes sense. Sell the cow and raise capital to put into arable farming. Pay off the staff and convert the buildings into luxury flats.'

'We don't have any staff. Or buildings.'

'Oh. Neither you do. Right, quick tap tap here and hey presto – bed and breakfast, that's the thing to get into. And sell the cow. Not to mention milk quota of course. Sell that for a pretty penny. Or about 28 pence a litre. What quota have you got?'

'I don't think we've got any.'

'Hmm. Pity. Lucky you haven't been penalised under the milk regulations. Still, you probably saved the £90 milking parlour inspection fee. What about silage effluent and the Water Authority – any trouble there?'

'No, we feed hay, but...'

'Thought so, typical regressive type. Still, you can sell the hay stocks off and plough out the grassland.'

'We're down to our last wisp of hay. I'm taking the cow to market this morning before my mother brains me.'

'Ah, taking my advice, eh. That'll be, quick tap tap on the old calculator, that'll be £3,000.'

'You've got to be joking. I was taking her anyway.'

'Ah, but now thanks to me and the computer you know you've made the right business decision. And here's a cash flow for you, with graphics. All right – I know a man of business when I see one – I'll settle for ten quid and a glass of milk.'

'Sorry – no milk. I want her bagged up when she goes into the sale ring. You can come for the walk if you like. Get up Buttercup. Get along there.'

'Look, I'll tell you what. Apart from being a management consultant and breeding pedigree Afghans I took a two day course as a seedsman. I'll get you started in arable farming.'

'How?'

'It so happens I have a sample of the coming crop. Basic seed, mark you. Look at that – superb, eh?'

'It's a bean.'

'Ah, but what a bean.'

'A solitary bean.'

'Yes, but that's a magic bean – early maturing, graded to

highest standards, dual purpose seed dressing.'

'How much do you want for it?'

'I'll take the cow, you take the bean. How about that?'

'Well, I don't know. She's a good cow.'

'Yes, but I'm saving you half a day at the mart and commission. Not to mention you won't need to pay luck money. And it's a good bean.'

'Right. Done.'

'You certainly have been – play on words there, old bean. Right – I've got the cow and you've got the bean. Two things to bear in mind – one, you'll need to be liberal with the growth regulator or you'll be in trouble. Two, that variety is very susceptible to chocolate spot so your spray costs will be a bit steep. But it'll make a good entry for wheat and you might be surprised by results.'

'Sounds like a fairytale to me, Chummy.'

'You said it Jack. Come on Buttercup. I think I'll paint you brown and sell you as a suckler. Here we go, here we go, here we go...'

The wet mists of time

An archaeologist writes: 'We made a significant find today in one of the many abandoned farm houses which abounded in the countryside in the twenty-first Century. It is the diary of a farmer's wife kept for a few brief weeks during the summer of 1987.

Her jottings were made at irregular intervals and apparently often at times of great stress and tension. However, I believe they provide us with a wonderful insight into life at that time when agriculture was in a state of flux and the weather, as referred to frequently in the notebook, was 'terrible', 'awful', 'worse' and 'even worse'.

As we now know this succession of wet summers in the 1980s was a meteorological freak which gave way by the turn of the century to the marvellous climatic conditions we have now.

But enough people, mainly in farming circles were unhinged enough at the time to form queues to jump off Rothbury Crags. Or to end the way this unfortunate lady did – but I anticipate. Now I quote:

JUNE 22. We cut our first hay. Heavy rain fell later. The next day it was torrential. Arthur sprained his thumb when dosing lambs, not sure how. We have had 90 hours' sunshine so far in June compared with a normal 200 hours. They say 1980 and 1982 were worse, but you can't believe everything you read in the papers.

JUNE 25. It stayed dry all day. Two lambs died. Arthur says winter barley rotten with mildew and wheat has yellow rust. Spring barley has black specks, stress symptom. Arthur asked me to check his back for black specks and rust. He said this was the last joke he would make this summer.

JULY 1. Dull and blustery. Turning hay. Wheel fell off the tractor. Went to stores for new bearings. Came back. Went back to stores for the right bearings. Collie limping.

JULY 7. We have had hot weather. Arthur got mild sunstroke when stooking hay. He is well pleased with his first hay. Cut second field tonight. Found slugs on spring barley. I think he said this was unusual, he was crying at the time about alternaria appearing on the oilseed rape.

JULY 10 and 11. Torrential rain. Some barley gone flat. Attendance at church fete affected. Two firsts and a second and should have had another first for jam. Arthur lost his temper at the quoits and bounced one off the vicar's head. He apologised, but the vicar was unconscious.

JULY 18. It has rained every day for a week except two. On those days we turned hay. Dull and cold. Botrytis on the peas. Arthur says this is something rot by any other name. He may have meant petal leaf fall rot.

JULY 22. We had 20 minutes of sun today. Helped dip the sheep. It went quite well until Dad and the Suffolk tup with the bent nose went into the dipper together. We got him out fairly quickly but it took a while to rake up his teeth. He wouldn't let me take him down to the doctors for a check over. He said worse things happen at sea and Arthur said we might as well be at something sea. It was raining again by then.

JULY 28. The strain of this weather is beginning to tell. Turned hay twice before it began to rain. Arthur kicked the hay-bob and grazed his shin quite badly. I was going to say that what we really need is a holiday, but decided to leave it for the time being. He's not eating much and the bottle of whisky Dad brought back from Islay seems to have disappeared.

JULY 29. Started to wash the curtains today, but turned hay instead then helping stook it. Arthur says it's canny hay after all. I thought it looked a right load of rubbish, but kept that to myself. At least we didn't burn it – it was probably too damp.

AUGUST 3. Quite good weather has brought the combines out in one or two places. Yesterday Arthur said they must be crackers. We had ours out today because the winter barley had ripened a lot overnight. There's a heap on the cattle shed floor you could make snowballs out of which Arthur thinks is canny. Sometimes I think I take a more realistic view of life than he does. In fact I think that if *we* ran the farms things would run more smoothly – apart from the weather of course which is awful.

AUGUST 6. Lovely harvest day. Dad on the trailer drove into the back of the combine which Arthur was reversing when he shouldn't have been. I ordered new straw walkers and a rear hood which are coming from the south tomorrow. Arthur went for a long walk but could hear combines in all directions. Lay on the bed with the curtains drawn until it got damp.

AUGUST 7. Straw walkers went up to Edinburgh and back to Durham by rail. Collected finally late evening. New hood is in a siding in Aberdeen. Arthur stayed rational while it was raining, but when combines started going again in the afternoon he pulled his jersey over his head and sank to his knees.

AUGUST 10. I read somewhere that men are just little boys in long trousers who play with different toys. I see what they mean – Arthur just sat and grinned all day on the combine in the sunshine and wouldn't even come off to eat his sandwiches. It's nice to see him happy even if the yield wasn't quite as good as he thought.

AUGUST 12. Glorious twelfth except if you're a grouse of course. Or a grouch like Arthur. It poured with rain all day. I think I'll stop keeping this diary. What with running about for spare parts, and answering the phone and pointing reps in the right direction and feeding Arthur and Dad and putting up with their filthy temper every time it rains or just because the bullocks got out this morning. I think I'll see if that nice management consultant we met at the NFU dinner is still looking for a secretary. To hell with harvest – I want to live a little.

The diary ends on this sad note. We can only surmise what happened to the un-named heroine, Arthur and Dad, even the management consultant. That reminds me of a good joke I heard the other day about consultants, but perhaps some other time.

Not altogether OK yah down on the old estate

'Wally! Old bean! Brill to see you. Haven't seen you in years.'

'No, I've...'

'Have a drink. That was quick. Have another.'

'Thanks. I will. Cheers.'

'And you. A third? Fine. No, no, I'll get them. Bit of gain on the yen recently. Well, well and how are you? Still staying ahead of the taxman?'

'Yes. No probs. It's staying ahead of Flora that's the trouble. Only the other night she said she dreamt she was married to a millionaire.'

'You're lucky – mine thinks that when she's awake. Ha, ha, ha!'

'No, but seriously...'

'Oh don't be serious. It's only money. My wife lost her Gold card the other month but I haven't reported it yet – whoever has it is spending less than she does! Go on – laugh. It'll do you good.'

'I don't laugh so much any more these days.'

'Probs? Gremlins? Customer resistance? Bank manager getting close to the truth?'

'No, it's the environment that worries me.'

'Environment? Here? Open a window. Have a quick blast on the old CFC-free aerosol.'

'No, no. Not here. The wild blue yonder. The great outdoors. What we live in. What people are doing to it.'

'My word, you've got it bad. I forgot. You live in the country now don't you? Really rural man.'

'Yes, but it's all changing. It was an idyll when we first

105

bought our wee estate...'

'Estate?'

'Yah. A house and three whole acres of rough grazing for the ponies. A dream come true.'

'Farmhouse I take it?'

'Natch. They sold off the land to one or two of the neighbouring sons of the soil and then sold off the farmhouses. Pretty clever stroke really.'

'And you've improved it of course.'

'Natch. Edwardian windows in, façade painted an ultra-tasteful old gold, Gothic bridge over a specially dug pond, rustic fencing, wrought iron, that sort of thing.'

'Sounds spot on.'

'It's super. And we made great efforts to fit in. Joined the village hall committee, sorted out the Rurals' finances, donated a cup named after my mother for the best sweet pea in the flower show, hosted the church coffee morning.'

'Made lots of friends?'

'Funnily enough, no. Strange lot these country types. Salt of the earth, mind you, salt of the earth. We just know they like us – deep down. And we did enjoy country living.'

'Did?'

'Do. Do enjoy country living. But it's all changing. The good old days are gone. Why, when we moved there we had the traditional harvest sounds almost on our doorstep – the roar of the combines, the screaming gear changes of the students driving the trailers. The clank of the baler. The smell of diesel. The smoke and ash from burning straw. It was vibrant. It was living.'

'I always say the old ways are best.'

'They are. The whine of the forage harvester, the blast of the grain drier, the hiss of slurry on the spring air. But it's all going.'

'Why?'

'It's all this diversification. It's everywhere. There's a rough terrain vehicle track on one side. War games on the other, splatting away at each other like ten-year-olds. We had the most lovely field of oilseed rape behind us – they've turned it into a golf course. There are 19 craft shops within a mile turning out hand-painted enamel brooches, chocolate teapots and polished pebbles on strings. There's a play park, and adventure park and a park park. Not only that, there's a butterfly farm, a fish farm, a snail farm and a health farm. There's a cashmere goat farm, an Angora rabbit farm and an exotic animal farm. The only thing we don't seem to have is a farm sort of farm. The countryside is going to the dogs before our eyes. Oh, my Fordson and my Clayson long ago...'

'There, there, old bean, don't get upset. I know it's a strain.'

'It is.'

'...but matter of fact we have a little project on the stocks you might be interested in – converting wooden henhouses into holiday chalets. Wally – don't jump out of the window. Was it something I said?'

As scarce as hen's teeth

When house buying, you are advised to inspect on a bad day. This is doubly true of farms.

The sun beating down, a classic coastal view, cattle at lush grass, crops throbbing with growth – these factors can take a potential buyer's mind off hard facts and into fantasy.

Not that I was thinking of buying land. But it isn't every day, if at all in the past ten years, that an 800-acre good-quality farm has come up for let on a full agricultural tenancy.

Because landowners are reluctant to lose control of their own property, in recent years we have seen the tenancy market virtually disappear.

Full tenancies, that is, where the farmer pays a rent and in return is in control of land and buildings for his lifetime and can then pass it on to the next two generations, are as scarce as hen's teeth.

In recent years we have had an increase in share-farming partnerships, with landlord and tenant having some agreement on work and capital for a fixed number of years.

More recently, Roxburghe Estates in the Borders let four hill farms to tenants on a retirement basis.

But a full tenancy is something else. As a result, most farmers in the area must have walked it on the four viewing days, either for their own benefit or ostensibly to give someone else the benefit of their experience.

Potential tenants also came from much further afield, north and south, like wasps round the honey pot.

It's too late to get the particulars and do a two-year cash flow now, so don't rush. I would guess that the landlord's agents will have at least 100 to sift through already.

The farm, run extensively by a long-established tenant, is a good example of a traditional mixed farm, with potential for good arable crops on at least half of it. The permanent pasture is good, and what is described in the particulars as rough grazing would not be sniffed at in many areas of Scotland as permanent pasture.

Thus do land agents differ from the hyperbole of estate agents.

It would, I suspect, have been a different prospectus if the exceptional farmhouse, ornamental lake and splendid

garden, along with 825 acres, had been for sale. No expert on these matters, I'm certain it would make a small fortune if sold to white settlers from the south.

By deciding to let it, the elderly landlord will make one person very happy – the one who gets it – and several hundred people miserable – those who tendered and didn't get it, and those who walked it, compared it with what they had at home and grew melancholy.

What was interesting was to watch the various approaches to the job in hand. And to watch how genuine contenders did their best to avoid each other, walking past with averted eyes or developing a sudden interest in the quality of the block-walling or a leaking water-trough.

That was round the elderly range of buildings, which, as one experienced farmer I knew used to point out, are not all that important. The land is what you make or break on.

Some walked the land thoroughly, in boots and shirt-sleeves. Some did it diffidently in shoes and sunglasses. Some used the pick-up or modest saloon; it is a long farm, with an excellent central road.

The real poser, not to mention pillock, drove round in his Volvo. He passed me several times – did I mention that I was there? – and I'll say this for a Volvo, that it handles rough terrain.

I don't mention the car or the man as a composite stereotype although he must be as close to the public idea of a typical farmer as I have had the misfortune to see for some time.

Expensively dressed in a crumpled way, bunnet square on his head, E-registration car and his wife doing the hopping in and out to open gates, gates which several people made a point of meticulously closing seconds before he might have thought it was deliberate.

He was almost a parody of himself. But he was real all right, proving this by butting in front of more polite types, who were hovering and waiting their turn, to interrogate the present tenant.

I have this wistful hope, and I put it no higher, that he is unsuccessful.

Whoever you were, and however inconspicuous you tried to be, someone would spot and identify you, pinpoint the family connections, estimate the value of your present set up, and forecast your chances of appearing on the short list.

I know that because it's what I did myself. It was a nice day for a farm walk.

In the name of conservation

I have two views about the state of the roadside verges at this time of year, a time I always think of as high summer regardless of what the weather is actually doing.

One view is that I thoroughly enjoy the riot of wild flowers like white and pink campions, clumps of dog-roses, mullions, occasional poppies, even the rampant purple willow-herb.

The opposing view is that I can't help wondering why the councils allow the verges to get into such a state and how much better they would look if tidily cut.

In a few parts of the area I've seen verges neatly cut and cleared, but those were the wide ones which some thrifty farmers use for hay. The average verge seems to get one slice of the mower through the rising tide of cigarette packets, newspapers, empty drink cans and so on and that is it.

There must be a reason and I suppose we'll be told it is the lack of money. But surely it can't cost that much to cut the verges thoroughly, tidying the countryside up and avoiding the risk of accidents at the many farm road and minor road junctions.

And there would still be a place for the wild flowers, particularly my favourite the dog-roses, close in to the hedges and fences.

I suppose the other reason which might be advanced for the generally deplorable state of country road verges is that the 'conservationists' are getting the upper hand.

There is an old story about the keen gardener who moved to a new house with a derelict garden which was a mass of weeds, nettles, rubble and bric a brac; which may remind some of you of what you should be doing instead of reading

111

this, but let that pass.

Within a year or so he had transformed the garden into neat rows of vegetables, clumps of flowers, borders and trimmed grass. The vicar was impressed and complimented the gardener on what he and the Lord had achieved.

Slightly peeved, the gardener replied: 'That's all very well, vicar but you should have seen it when the Lord had it to himself.'

That's how I feel about our land. There is a place for wildlife and the plants we think of as weeds and there is room for farmers to make more effort in some directions.

But to be productive and profitable crops and grassland must be well managed. Grass fields full of dockens, buttercups, ragwort and daisies may look pretty from the road, but they won't fatten lambs or cattle particularly well.

Likewise a cereal crop hidden by wild oats and white and yellow mayweed may look aesthetically pleasing on the skyline, but won't produce a pretty sample or much of a profit.

There has to be some commonsense on both sides. I suggest that many farmers have been on the right road to start with and in the past few years, with the publicity given to conservation and the formation of bodies like the Farming, Forestry and Wildlife Advisory groups they have gone even further.

Now it's time for the vociferous conservationists to ease off. I often wonder what their homes and gardens look like or how they would take it if we started advising them on what to do with their property, whether owned or tenanted.

I also look at what has been done in some of our town and city centres in the past few years and wonder what right any group has to complain about the countryside when they allow some of the eyesores we are all familiar with to develop.

Or simply appear. Some of the worst blots I've seen in any town are shop signs in Berwick high street; when they take the worst ones down I'll start wearing a tee-shirt saying 'I'm a conservationist'.

While waiting for that to happen, we're also waiting for harvest which may just be rather quicker than we expected even a week or so ago. The continued dry, if variable, weather continues to ripen winter barley or burn it out and the earlier oilseed rape crops may be ready for swathing well before the end of July.

As usual, the crows can't wait. They've been pouring in like bomber squadrons despite banger guns and ropes, wires, tapes, plastic bags and shotguns.

An uninterrupted hour or two of several hundred of those big feet tramping the edges of a field makes a depressing mess; and every farmer is convinced he's got every crow in the Borders and the North of England. They can't have, of course – w ve got them all.

The paradox of life

The jargon is 'a spraying window'. To me, and probably you, it means a spell of weather when the ground and the days are dry enough to get on and spray.

It figures that the number of available 'windows' at this time of year tend to be few compared with, for example, May or July.

On second thoughts, forget July. But it is true that if spraying chances are not taken in September they become rarer during October and November.

This must be the reason for the flush of sprayers over the weekend and at the beginning of this week. Almost ideal overhead conditions except for a slightly too strong breeze at times and almost dry ground underwheel.

After trying to resist I was out there with them, applying manganese to winter barley in one field and hoping to kill off weeds in another.

My original theory was that pre-emergence sprays, which go on as soon as the crop has been drilled, and kill off weed seedlings as they germinate, could be given a miss this year.

The theory was based on the fact that two fields sprayed with pre-emergence last year had to be sprayed again in the spring. Also that avoiding a spray now meant about five months' saving on a debt to be carried or money borrowed.

Unfortunately the weeds didn't hear about the theory. They have emerged and thrived to the point where they are beginning to pose a threat to the crop.

At least I think they are, which is much the same thing. As a result we decided to spray after all and the wonderful 'window' in the weather was a great help.

It must be as pleasant a spell as I can remember in this

month. The old saying goes: 'November ice to bear a duck, the rest of the winter slush and muck'.

If we take the reverse to be true, which I'm sure is what we should do with these old sayings, then we're in for a hard winter.

In saying that I'm reminded of the opinion a bus-driver friend had of old sayings and those who spout them. He was passing the time with an old countryman who pointed happily to mole-hills in the December sunshine.

'Ah,' said the old boy, 'the moles know. Fine weather ahead.'

Next day as the bus tried to follow the snow plough through a foot of snow the driver mused on the ways of moles and the ramblings of old countrymen.

I've reached the stage of taking the weather as it comes and almost ignoring forecasts, seaweed and octogenarian advice.

Often enough I have a fair idea of what the weather will do, not from any prolonged study of the signs but simply a feeling in my bones.

It's not infallible, but a lifetime of experiencing weather at close quarters must produce a subconscious response to certain conditions. I think I'm every bit as likely to be right as something small and furry digging underground.

The weather produced one of those countryside paradoxes which would please the 'isn't nature wonderful' brigade, of which I am not one.

Michael Parkinson once summed it up when writing about cricket, which he played successfully in the Yorkshire leagues. His experiences there convinced him that cricket was not the sweet and crinolined lady some enthusiasts would have us believe; she was a cynical bitch full of nasty surprises.

I feel like that about nature. I don't believe it's wonderful, I believe that over the years it compensates and produces moments of beauty as well as days of misery and mud.

The paradox I saw when ploughing was the midden – long, low and unperfumed – covered along its length with gossamer which moved gently in the morning sun. A rat popped its head out of a hole for a speedy survey and two cock pheasants were knocking hell out of each other on top of it.

A Sunday newspaper used to boast, and perhaps still does, that 'all human life is here'. It seemed for a few minutes until the rat disappeared and the pheasants got tired of what they were doing to each other, that a lot of nature was on the midden.

Even when they had gone the gossamer remained. For a while.

Then and now

I believe that people know their own business best. When I see a combine cutting wheat in the rain in August that belief is tested.

No doubt they are doing the right thing. I had it patiently explained to me that if the wheat was potentially a good milling sample it was worthwhile to cut it at high moisture content – they weren't joking there – then dry it down gently.

Fine, but I still think it looked silly. It's one more example of the Mastermind syndrome: 'I've started so I'll finish'.

It's a bit like housework, not that I'm an expert on that either. There are far more labour-saving devices than there used to be, but the rush to get things done seems greater with each passing year.

As far as I recollect no one would ever have thought of cutting wheat or barley at much above 20 per cent moisture content at one time, never mind above 25 per cent.

It is quite common now. We have combines that will clear 60 acres a day, but panic more than when a 12-acre day was good going.

It has to do with acreages partly. Instead of 100 or 150 acres of spring barley and that was it, many farms in this part of the world now grow several hundred acres of cereals and oilseed. Quite a few grow more than 1000 acres.

That sort of acreage weighs on the mind; eventually it requires more presence of mind to stop the combines than to keep them going. Hence the sight of one cutting wheat in the rain. In August!

It's going to be September before ours gets cut. As far as I can see it won't be ripe for another week at least, never

117

mind dry.

It doesn't always pay to wait. We know that. But given a chance it is surprising how often sun and wind will do much of the drying of the crop even in a bad year.

One of the pleasures of harvest, and there are some, is freshly baled straw going into the cattle. The last of last year's bales, stored outside, are getting a bit tired by now.

The cattle inside on a barley diet and the young calves being reared in group pens seem to appreciate the fresh straw as much as we do.

Big round bales have certainly made the straw harvest an easier job. Once baled, fields can either be cleared at leisure if the following crop is a spring one or cleared fairly quickly by one tractor driver with a double-spike on the back.

The speed and lack of need for manual labour compares favourable with all but the most sophisticated methods of handling small rectangular bales. Round bales also rule out the necessity of building stacks or building loads on a lorry.

I was never a good stack builder. If all the corners stayed in it was more luck than skill. Occasionally I would stand on top as bales flowed up the elevator and wonder where to put the one I had in my hand at the time.

Various suggestions would be made from the bottom of the elevator and not all of them had anything to do with the stack.

I preferred building them into a shed, particularly one with three solid sides which meant I only had to worry about the front falling out. Building a lorry load was a problem I tried to avoid.

Thankfully, many lorry drivers can build a good load of small bales. And between them and the forklift operators they also put on a good load of big round bales.

It strikes me as one more example of a new country skill. We admire the workers and farmers – in some cases the same – who used to build elegant stacks with sheaves. They adapted to building stacks with bales.

Now there is a fair degree of skill in building 52 big round bales onto a lorry.

Times and methods change and it is no good forever looking back and exclaiming how skilful men were with their hands. If they had been given the chance of using labour saving equipment they would have taken it.

If the Egyptians had had cranes and ready-mixed concrete they would have used them when they built the Pyramids. No one would have been happier than the slaves winching the blocks into place by hand!

Nothing so queer as folk

Seven of our fields adjoin two busy roads. I suspect that this gives us more chance to observe, and worry about, the public than vice versa.

It is true that quite a lot of the passing traffic is local and rural. But at this time of year large numbers of tourists and visitors pass by, including those which use the layby.

While we were preparing a field for oilseed rape, an operation which involved ploughing, discing, crumbling and three passes with the rollers before we were finished, I had plenty of time to watch those who stopped.

None behaved particularly badly, although the British habit of throwing rubbish on the ground when it would be easier to put it in the large bin provided was prevalent.

One or two made discreet use of the hedge, which was understandable, a few had dogs which they kept on a lead, one produced a gas burner and kettle, one left a flask behind.

But what they all had in common, from elderly couples to a giggle of teenagers, was a lack of interest in what was going on around them.

I couldn't help thinking that if I was walking down a busy street I would look in the shops to see what was going on. A building site or small factory at work would be looked at.

Our passing travellers hardly looked up or around. We had two tractors going in the field. A baler was working on the other side of the road, and for a time a sprayer was at work applying desicant to peas – and a forklift was loading bales onto an articulated lorry.

As far as I could see, it passed them by. They could have been on the hard shoulder of a dual carriageway for all the

difference it made.

In one of the busiest times of the year on the farm, I thought that there would have been something of interest. As the saying goes, there is nothing so queer as folk.

When they did notice us, of course, was when we got onto the road with tractors or machinery. When this happens, and desperate drivers are thwarted over perhaps quarter of a mile of a 200-mile journey, I'm reminded of two things.

One is Piet Thien's small ode to a dead roadhog: 'Here lies extinguished in his prime, a victim of modernity. Yesterday he hadn't time, now he has eternity'.

The second is a memory of a trip to Ireland some years ago when a convoy of visitors' cars was held up by a man with a donkey cart holding the centre of a country lane. We were advised that waiting until the cart turned off in its own time was the only thing to do.

The same should be true of farm machinery on roads. We

don't like being there unless it is the only possible way of getting to another field. Most of us are on the road for a mile at most. All it needs is a little patience.

That is what morotists have not got. The urge to pass a slow moving vehicle despite double white lines and oncoming traffic is too great. They will pass right up to within ten yards of the village roundabout, slam on the brakes and cut in.

The same applies to coming onto the roundabout. Cars will race onto it almost under the weight box on the front of the tractor. Likewise, they will shoot out of side roads in front of a tractor.

It either upsets them or presents a challenge, I'm not sure which. Either way, they do it.

All this being true, it was tempting to ignore the family with a camping trailer which broke down near suicide corner. This is a bending stretch of road between two banks where cars, vans, and occasionally lorries, career straight on – into our field from one direction, into a neighbour's from the other.

It is known as the Goslaw Cut, Goslaw being a corruption of the original field name on the other side of the road which was Goose Law. It would be a brave, or extremely stupid goose which made the attempt to cross the cut now.

With traffic flashing past at alarming speed as usual, the family were frantically trying to decide what to do and divert vehicles at the same time.

Feeling rather like the Lone Ranger – or what he might be like on a 95 horse power Silver wearing a boiler suit – I moseyed across, got the details, and contacted Angus at the farm on the CB.

He contacted the motoring organisation and later welded up their trailer to send them on their way, late but happy, and impressed with on-farm efficiency and friendliness.

Perhaps next time at least one family will study more than their sandwiches.

Scoring points to make the grade

When you have a student working on the farm, the college isn't satisfied with a brief assurance that they have been satisfactory. They send out a twenty point questionnaire.

What should worry farmers is whether the student is also given a report to fill in on his or her employer.

'Time keeping: not bad, but variable. Crack of dawn sometimes, says he's been delayed by a phone call the next. At dinner times a lot depends on how the Test match is going. Say fair.

'Application and effort: From frenzied to lackadaisical.

'Use of initiative: What's the choice? I suppose it has to be excellent. I've never seen a man do more with a pocketful of nails and a couple of bits of string. The only trouble is we shouldn't have had that trouble with the mill and mix plant in the first place, but I suppose that'll come under another heading.

'Learning ability: They haven't got a nil grading. I haven't been able to teach him anything in fourteen months and goodness knows I've tried hard enough. Poor – and that's being kind.

'Reliability: When do they mean? If I'm making a good job of something I never see him. The first time I make a mistake and he appears round the corner like a guided missile. I suppose he usually manages to sort things out if I'm in a muddle.

'Attention to detail: Takes infinite pains if it's my work he's studying. If it's something he's doing, says that a man on a galloping horse wouldn't notice. Fair.

'Job potential in this area: How do you spell infinitesimal? I guess he's got potential as a farmer, but he'd be struggling trying to do anything else. Fair.

'Hygiene: Good, but it's really his wife that should get the credit. He'd wear a boilersuit till it fell off. I know he would because that was what it was like the fortnight she was in hospital. He was a walking disaster area until she came back on crutches.

'Tidiness: Hold me up. He tries I'll give him that. As long as there's not too much happening on the farm for about one week in every six months it's quite tidy. But as soon as we're busy it's heap lie on. Rating poor.

'Ability to communicate: Not bad if he'd only tell me once. But before I do it he tells me three different ways to do the job. For good measure once I've made a start he comes and tells me a fourth time with variations. I would say over-communicative.

'Need for supervision: Yes – constantly. You never know what he'll be getting up to next.

Effort: Frantic.

'Attitude: Thoroughly well-motivated. He says that his overdraft gives him great inspiration. It's the modern equivalent of the slave driver's whip.

'Manual dexterity: Sorry fell off the stool there. Wonderful. Superb. Marvellous. Anything which can be hit with a hammer is at risk. I watched him try to refill a grease-gun. It would have been a sensation at the Paladium. I do wish they'd put a nil category on this questionnaire.

'When given a job is it finished within the expected time or not: That depends. If it's an important job, yes. If it's one he's not very fussy about, no. He'll wait until I've finished what I'm doing and get me to finish it.

'Acquires new skills quickly or slowly: Where's the column for not at all? That's not strictly true but there's not enough room to write if there's money in it he'll learn quickly.

'Mechanical aptitude: A similar rating to manual dexterity.

'Ability with livestock: Well now this depends mainly on what sort of fettle he's in. He can be very good, and patient when things are running his way. But on a bad day he's liable to do things with a stick that he regrets. Better say fair to variable.

'Would I work for him at some future date: That's a poser. A bit like the livestock. On his good days I would. On his bad days I'd rather work for Nigel Lawson.

'Does he get on well with other farmers: His yields vary a lot, like his lambing percentages, depending on who he's talking to. Mind you so do theirs. They're only kidding themselves really. I suppose he gets on all right with most of them.

'With further training is he capable of further responsibility: I'll have to give this question further consideration. Please allow two years for an answer.'

A dead loss to farming?

If most people who have obituaries written about them could come back and read them, they would be surprised.

This seems particularly true of farming where there is no shortage of salt of the earth characters, bathed in warmth, love and respect. And all you have to do to earn these accolades is drop dead. It seems simple enough.

The wonder is where all these salts of the earth hide themselves while alive, though hide is probably the wrong word for some of the aggressive, mean, greedy, rude or plain miserable types who are cordially hated while breathing, but qualify for eulogies as soon as they stop.

It probably has something to do with superstition about speaking ill of the dead, though I prefer the attitude of one farmer who refused to attend his father-in-law's funeral on the grounds that he had never liked the old bee while he was alive and saw no reason to change his mind now.

This isn't to argue that no one ever deserves a glowing obituary; it is to say that some of the biggest twerps get the most coverage on the basis that it is better to have been a successful man than to have been a good man.

In the days when there were such things there was a saying that no man was a hero to his valet. You can adapt that for farming by saying that no man is a hero to his neighbours.

No matter how high he climbs in NFU politics or committee chairmanships or how successful at empire-building and nepotism, his neighbours know the truth, or most of it. They're the ones falling under the table when they read the final obituary of this wise, generous and benevolent man. To think they'd lived next door for thirty years and never knew.

But it's hard to know who to blame for the obituary which contains more terminological inexactitudes than a politician's speech; like pedigree stock breeders who attempt to show their sheep or cattle in natural condition instead of blow-waved and manicured, the truthful obituary writer would simply be begging for trouble.

And they have to start somewhere. There will be some kind of potted biography on file giving committees, chairmanships, acts of wisdom and so on, but to get the human touch a few comments from someone who knew the late great man is needed. The neighbour is an obvious choice:

'Sorry to trouble you with a phone call at this time of night, but I believe you knew The Late Great quite well?'

So the drink and the women have caught up with him at last, have they? Not before time. I'm surprised he reached sixty: 'Yes, indeed. I did know the Late Great quite well.'

'Would you call yourself a close friend?'

I didn't know he had any friends, never mind close ones. I wonder if they'll have to sell that bottom fifty acres? That would be handy: 'Well, reasonably close. We were neighbours for many years, of course.'

'And how would you describe him as a man?'

I wouldn't describe him as a man at all, more a corkscrew. And as rude as they come: 'One of the old school, I would say. Not afraid to speak his mind and with a keen eye for a bargain.'

'He seemed to work very hard, on behalf of other farmers and on his farm, so that in some ways he was his own worst enemy?'

Not while about 300 people I could name were still alive. He never worked for anybody unless he could see a shilling in it for himself. And there usually was: 'Yes, he pushed himself to the limit. He'll be a great loss to farming.'

'Well, thank you for filling in some of the background to the Late Great. This must be a very sad day for you.'

Just wait till you hang up and I'll see if I can still turn

somersaults: 'Yes, his type are the salt of the earth and the backbone of farming.'

Anatomy of a visit to the Smithfield extravaganza

Leaving Smithfield Show last Wednesday I picked up a diary which had been dropped by an exhibitor.

Being nosy, I naturally read it. As the large cheque I asked for has not been sent, I have no option but to publish lengthy extracts starting today:

'Sunday a.m. Arrived on early morning train. Slight fuzziness caused by faulty heating system and poor-quality water. Carried Dan off train complaining of severe pains. Helped him take lighted pipe from his trouser pocket. Ran tongue – mine – under cold tap for ten minutes, picked up Dan and got taxi to Earls Court.

'Asked driver if he was asking for a fare or deposit on the cab. A Cockney phrasebook would help. They all think they're Arthur Daley. London gets less like Auchnagatt every year.

'Sunday p.m. Relaxing day. Dan so relaxed he almost fell apart. Overseas visitors reception v. good. The girl at the desk thought we were Romanian. Would have been better if Dan hadn't told the French attaché what he thought of French lamb. Bum's rush from reception a humiliating experience. Dan complained to show organisers. Bum's rush from organiser's office a humiliating experience. Took complaint to highest authority. Bum's rush from the lift a humiliating experience.

'Found our way to cattle lines where Will had everything under control. Cattle looking well. A supreme championship seems a certainty. Hope I feel better tomorrow.

'Monday a.m. V. early a.m. Up and about, trying not to lean forward in case my eyeballs drop out. Saw Dan's note

129

beside the soap: "This is the worst chewing gum I've ever tasted." Tried to wake him. He insisted he was dead. I said no. He said: "Well I wish I was." Left him to recover. Brisk walk to show.

'Some time brushing and combing the cattle until Will said he'd rather get it wrong by himself. Decided to make serious study of machinery options available at show.

'Monday p.m. Made serious study of machinery options. This took some time. Salesmen v. friendly and anxious to help. Discreet waving of chequebook made them even more friendly and anxious to help. One held the book while two others tried to guide my pen-hand, but I managed to escape. They tell me sales are v. good this year and if I don't buy a new tractor now there might not be any left. Placed an order for a new set of spanners.

'Ran back to cattle lines to help Will bring them out. He said: "Go away, that was hours ago." (He didn't really say go away, but I'm sure he didn't mean what he did say.) He said he'd already said it to Dan about half an hour earlier. Found Dan relaxing beside the gate at the judging ring. Seemed happy, so I left him. Most of the cattle seemed to avoid stepping on him.

'Stuck my head in a bucket of water for a few minutes. Felt much better, if rather damp. Helped Will settle the cattle down for the night. We collected two highly-commended tickets and third. I said: "Does this mean no supreme champion?" Will said "No" and one or two other things I'm sure he'll regret when he has time to reflect. Carried Dan back to the hotel.

'Tuesday a.m. The water here must be the worst in the world. Seldom felt so ill. One or two small whiskies would not have this effect. Dan, ridiculously cheery this morning, said "No, two small whiskies couldn't. It was the many large ones and the vindaloo extra special followed by the doner-kebab and monster-burger that did the damage".

'I have no recollection of them. Dan just laughed and poked me gently in the stomach then wished he hadn't.

"There's a lot to be said for a drink, he said. Imagine being teetotal and knowing when you wake up that that's the best you're going to feel all day." I think I'll try it.

'Tuesday p.m. Didn't win supreme championship. Will not speaking to anyone today. Settled cattle down early and we left early, determined to make the most of our last night in London. Brought new suit for the occasion. And tie. And shirt. Took great care with shaving. Now indistinguishable from the smooth, cultivated city types. I'd be a sensation in Rose Street.

'Three of us – Will speaking again – set out in great style for heart of the city. Decided Finsbury Park wasn't it – took wrong tube. Decided Piccadilly might be. Took cab to Soho and admired Buckingham Palace, Hyde Park, London Zoo, Tower Bridge and Docklands. Club owner shouted as we walked down this extremely interesting street: "Great show tonight boys – half price to farmers". I blame Dan's yellow dealer's boots. He said it was my tartan waistcoat. Will said it was our pointy heads. He's not enjoying this trip at all. Back late to hotel. Carried Dan into breakfast.

'Wednesday p.m. Don't remember a.m. much. Will in charge of the cattle. Met our banker on bank stand. Had a chat. He lent me the return train fare on condition I gave him the chequebook...'

Mud on wellingtons
signals delay

I suppose you can get used to anything. What worries me is that we may become amphibious as the mud and lying water refuses to dry up.

Boots have been kicked into a corner and forgotten. An indication of what sort of day it is can be had from the high-tide mark on the wellingtons.

The mud seems to make every job take twice as long, except that of changing dual wheels. This takes about four times as long, and is twice as messy.

These extra wheels fit on to the existing back wheels of both our main tractors. Once in place, they are an asset in any kind of field cultivations, particularly in a wet season because they spread the weight of tractor and machine over a much greater tyre area.

The snag with dual wheels is that they are heavy and unwieldy. The screw-in metal centre has to be matched exactly with the five brackets welded onto the tractor wheel.

It is this matching up which causes the perspiration, frustration, and desperation. On concrete in dry weather, fitting the duals can be carried out single-handed by one man unless the wheel actually falls over.

But trying to transfer a muddy set of wheels from one tractor to the other in a field in wet weather is not a job for a weakling. In fact, it is not a job for anyone in their right mind. Farmers and students trying to get their winter wheat drilled somehow in November no longer come into that latter category.

As a result, with a mixture of frenzy and fury, we

managed the trick not once, but twice as we got another twenty acres in during a day which ranks high on the list of those days where not a lot went right.

A dual wheel falling off was a start. The diesel leak came a good second. The tractor getting a flat tyre while the leak was being repaired could have been the final straw on a normal day.

Instead, that was reserved for the tractor we have on loan, burning out its clutch within an hour of coming into use to replace the one with diesel leak and flat tyre.

These defects had been repaired by the time we towed the burnt-out case onto a stubble field – and we soldiered on.

As can happen on days like that, a calm did follow the storm of mishaps. As darkness fell, we finally managed to settle into the rhythm which had been missing all day, with the crumbler going on ahead and the grain drill following steadily behind.

There was a sting in the tail of course. About 10.30 on a

clear, calm evening with only the headrigs to do, the crumbler clogged solid in a wet patch then fell off as a clippin sheared through.

It had been a long day, and we called it a night. That was a mistake. Forecast light showers turned into the usual downpour and it was five days before I got back to the headrigs.

This rate of painfully slow progress seems to have been going on for months. The hours, days and weeks go by in a haze of effort, but there is not a lot to show for it at any given time.

That view may simply be depression. I can't recall having as miserable a harvest and autumn drilling. This is not due simply to yields being poor to mediocre, although they have been.

The final wheat yield was 55 cwts an acre dried weight, and protein peas barely half a ton. Spring barley was 41 cwts an acre, oilseed rape 23 cwts, and winter barley slightly more than 60 cwts an acre as far as we can judge.

As we all become more cost-conscious, yield alone is not the sole criterion. What it cost to get it is vital. But as most farmers know it is the unthrifty and unhealthy animal which makes less and costs more to keep. It is the same with crops.

More disease pushed up the cost of sprays to control them. Levy, transport and drying charges meant that an on-farm price of £107 for wheat became a net return of less than £90 a tonne.

Malting barley sales helped us, but you don't need to be a financial genius to calculate that half-a-tonne of protein peas per acre at £185 per tonne before deductions has lost a lot of money.

We're now off to a poor start for next year by having to squeeze wheat into soft seedbeds, though most of the 108 acres of winter barley is looking well when it has been possible to see it through the interminable mist or drizzle. It's being so cheerful that keeps us going.

A bird in the hand

As has been said so many times before one of the best things to be said about plucking turkeys is that it keeps your mind off Christmas.

It's not easy. Keeping your mind off Christmas, that is, when every commercial television programme is studded with adverts and every B.B.C. one begins and ends with trailers for what is on at Christmas.

Newspapers are filled with adverts for new computers and the second hand columns are awash with last year's presents. Radio programmes have self-promoting adverts sprinkled through them like lucky charms in a Christmas pudding.

Children are brainwashed into thinking about little else. Shops struggle for trade. There's so much artificial festive good cheer going about that I'm surprised no one has drowned in the syrup.

Plucking turkeys, and other poultry, isn't easy either but it keeps you away from the worst of all this rubbishy gushing and frothing. For several days you may not even see much daylight, going into the plucking shed in semi-darkness and finishing in complete darkness.

Although at the time it doesn't feel like it plucking them is the easy part; but perhaps I should rephrase that for the benefit of all those who have been spending six to ten hours a day pulling feathers in cold sheds!

Physically, it's not easy. It's hard on the fingers, the back, the feet and the legs. A tea break when and if it comes is welcome. So is dinner time and tea time.

It's not too bad mentally if the birds are going to the mart. Trade may be good, mediocre or bad, but unless it is appalling – which can happen – the birds will find a buyer.

The hard part every year if you sell birds to private customers is to match the order to the birds available.

Thinking back, which seems to get harder as I get older, I can't help feeling it used to be easier. People ordered a turkey and that was more or less it.

In the past twenty years or so when the precise size of chicken or frozen turkey you want can be bought at any time of the year, Christmas buyers of fresh turkey expect the same.

With, say, 300 turkeys to meet about the same numbers of orders, it can't be done.

It particularly can't be done when the birds arrive ten days early as chicks and a mild winter encourages them to put on more weight than expected. Every year you try harder to get it right and every year there's some reason why it doesn't work out exactly as planned.

There must be easier ways to turn a few pounds. But in what the experts call the present economic climate it's not easy thinking of them.

At the time of writing, between plucking sessions, there haven't been any local marts for poultry. Prices last year were good so here's hoping for a repeat performance. I'm practising the resolution I've resolved to make in the New Year to look on the bright side.

If we weren't selling turkeys it might be a good time to advise people to stock a freezer with pheasants. Not being a shooting man, or a pheasant eating fan, I wasn't aware until the weekend that there is a glut of them this year.

A good summer for wild birds and possibly many more being reared has been too much of a good thing. I'm told that prices as low as 50p a bird can't find buyers.

This might have something to do with a puzzling raffle at a local concert I was at last week. A brace of pheasants used to be a good prize in a country raffle; last week four people saw their ticket pulled out as a winner and asked for the prize to go back into the draw.

I've seen that done with one of those bottles of aftershave

or tins of ratatouille which have been on the raffle circuit for some years, but not with pheasants.

It's either a glut of pheasant or a sign of the times that no one fancies the plucking and gutting involved. The brace found a taker at the fifth attempt, but it was a close thing.

It makes me wonder a little more about pheasant rearing and shooting. A small group walking farm land to shoot whatever wild pheasants are there is one thing.

Rearing them by the thousand, charging large sums for people to shoot them and having to chase the reluctant birds into the air to give the guns the chance to do it is another.

When a pheasant has spent several months being fed it must come as a shock that it's expected to waddle into the air to get its head blown off. At least with turkeys there's no pretence.

Off to work we go

One of the farming papers ran a competition among its readers for the best Christmas story. As someone who favours the realistic, down-to-earth, slurry on your boots type of writer I was disappointed by the winners.

They were almost all ghost stories, unrequited love or some such with the routine twist at the end. There was very little there about what every farmer and stockman knows Christmas really means, as summed up in the lines from the poem:

> I slept and dreamed
>   that life was beauty,
> I woke and found that
>   life was duty

The writers were given the first phrase with which to start their entry; Albert started his but never finished it for reasons which will become obvious. He gave me permission to use his crumpled manuscript, or ms as we literary types say, after he retrieved it from the collie's kennel.

We were just sitting down to Christmas dinner when...well, that's a laugh for a start. Time for a quick gallop round the kitchen and out again with a drumstick in one hand and six chippolatas in the other and Dorothy shouting something about stuffing.

Actually, it started long before that. I've had this calf with a touch of cold on and off for a few days, well possibly pneumonia. He'd had everything except valium and was recovering quite nicely, very canny in fact.

Christmas morning as you know was lovely. Beautiful.

Mildest for years I would say with the sun shining in a blue sky.

That was later of course. When I went out it was so dark I could hardly see. That was when I opened my eyes. But it was a lovely morning all right.

The big store cattle were pleased to see me. They'd knocked the ballcock off again and there was a bit of a pool at one end, but that didn't take long to fix. No, what got Christmas day off to its usual good start was that little calf lying peacefully in the corner.

Oh he was peaceful all right – also stiff as a board, dead as a dodo, beyond human aid. Laugh? I thought I'd never stop, but there's only so much time for unbridled merriment when there's stock to feed and I still had the sheep to go to.

So I did, whistling cheerfully, glancing at the sky and murmuring nil illegit carborundum meaning nobody in particular except perhaps Anthony clever clogs Rosen with his Latin quotes in Farming News, our great industry's answer to The Sun.

So I got to the sheep, managed to open the gate onto the turnip break without maiming myself, and shot through in a spray of mud. You know how clatchy it was.

Even losing a wellington half way along the boxes with a bag of feeding wasn't so bad – wet, uncomfortable, but not so bad. I don't know if you've ever tried putting on a wellington half full of mud and the other half full of sheep...I can't think of the word, but it's messy.

Now if the tractor had a diesel gauge that worked the next bit wouldn't have happened. Namely, and to wit, getting half way through the gateway in axle deep mud and running out of diesel.

The run up the road to haul Bill away from his loved ones, or in this case his family, did me good. I think. I haven't run like that for years and it was all I could do to stop him from giving me mouth to mouth resus...ressusc... re...the kiss of life. If you knew Bill you'd know the heart attack was preferable, but I digress if that's the word.

I know it wasn't his fault the tractor in the shed had a flat battery, and I did apologise later for what I said to him. But he might at least have remembered where I had put the jump leads the last time. I found them eventually of course, hanging behind the bruiser in the granary just where you would expect them to be.

We got it started no bother after that, well, no more than two or three shots and a few sparks to get them on the right way round. It's not easy to see these little plus and minus signs on older batteries.

Halfway down we saw the stragglers just coming out of the gateway the tractor was stuck in. They might have had the decency to come towards the farm, but you know what sheep are like. Luckily there wasn't much traffic on the main road that morning and Bill's a fair sprinter when he's in the mood.

No, we got them back in not too badly, not much after dinner time really. What really spoiled the day was when the chain snapped as we towed it out of the gateway and Bill shot through the hedge on the other side of the road because he was looking over his shoulder at me.

So we were just sitting down to Christmas dinner when I thought I don't remember seeing a herd of Limousins on that winter wheat before...thanks, dear, I'll just have the pudding in this hand and the custard in my...oh well suit yourself.

Another fine mess

'Tidings of comfort and joy, comfort and joy, Oh tidings of comf...'

'Hoi! Push off.'

'Just a little seasonal greeting there, just two honest people trying to earn a crust at this festive time of year.'

'You're too late. We're getting some serious drinking in for the end of the year. Now push off.'

'Right. Fine. How about a little something to help us along?'

'Will a foot do? Try this.'

'Right. Wonderful. No thanks, we're just off. Goodbye. Okay, we can stop jogging now.'

'Good. I'm about whacked. Well, we can cross carol singing off the diversification list. Another fine mess you nearly got us into.'

'Sorry. It seemed a good idea at the time.'

'You're an optimist Bob, I'll give you that. Failure doesn't weigh you down the way it does ordinary mortals.'

'Don't forget I've been a farmer for twenty years. I'm used to the slings and arrows of outrageous fortune...'

'Not to mention the supports and subsidies of the outrageous Common Market.'

'Now don't you start. If I'm so well off how come I'm carol singing round the pubs at the end of December?'

'Because you're crackers probably. And I'm just as silly for going with you. Let's go home.'

'Might as well I suppose. It hasn't been the success I hoped for and that's a fact.'

'No, it's been almost as bad as the Catch Your Own Turkey fiasco.'

'Well I thought that if it works in fish restaurants why

shouldn't it work with Christmas dinners? I mean if you can point to a trout in a tank and get it on a plate...'

'Rainbow trout don't weigh 20 lbs on the hoof.'

'Claws – turkeys have claws, not hooves. Ow!'

'As I was saying – 20 lb and more on the hoof. Some considerably more as you'd misjudged the hatching date. Your average suburban man doesn't want to see his turkey except on a tray in the oven. How many came?'

'Oh, quite a lot – dozens – nearly – seven to be exact.'

'How many caught their turkey?'

'Er...let me see now...'

'Three. And how many are suing you for cuts, abrasions and injury to the person?'

'Er...now...'

'Three. So what did we do? Had to pluck them all ourselves and send them to the mart at the last minute. Or at least I did because you broke a thumb catching the first one.'

'Be fair...'

'I am. We broke even because it was a good year at the marts. Still, it was better than Chop down your own Christmas tree, as advertised with details in the local paper.'

'Now that...'

'So two men with muffled chainsaws or a sharp breadknife take you at your word and cut down 1,000 trees overnight and disappear with them.'

'Look, we're being told to diversify. Traditional farming is on the way out. They don't want the crops and livestock we've been producing – very successfully I might add for some considerable time.'

'Don't tell me – you did it all for the good of the country.'

'Not exactly. We managed to scrape off a little each year as the wheel went round.'

'Please – my glass eye's starting to water.'

'It's true – you don't make a fortune on a place our size. And for the past few years we've had to run harder just to make a living. That's why I'm diversifying.'

'So successfully too? The goat breeding was a sensation?'

'Not absolutely precisely a sensation. Perhaps we invested a little too much too quickly...'

'And found you had an infertile buck of the wrong kind?'

'He didn't look infertile.'

'He didn't act infertile either as several terrified visitors would testify. But he was.'

'Still, I got a sweater out of it. Admittedly, it pongs a bit, but outside in a strong wind it's not so bad.'

'Deer farming. Don't forget the deer farming. Is that butcher's cold store still full of venison?'

'Slight problem with the marketing, certainly, bit ahead of our time perhaps...'

'Fish farming? The only man in Britain to try a drypond fish farm.'

'Not exactly dry. Admittedly, the water supply was a little erratic to be totally successful...'

'Yes. Trying to cram them into cattle troughs and the sheep dipper in times of shortage didn't really work either did it?'

'Not exactly...'

'And the Clay Pigeon shooting range and the War Games course – for both of which you narrowly escaped tarring and feathering on a Sunday afternoon by the local home owners who have paid for the privilege of living out of town.'

'A shooting range is good enough for that lot. I should have arranged to use them as targets.'

'You may be right at that. But the law agreed with them. Which left you the caravan site.'

'For which I couldn't get permission. Or the golf course.'

'Which left bed and breakfast. Another roaring success.'

'I thought they'd like an authentic farmhouse breakfast – overalls on the back door, wellingtons roasting by an open cooker, the ruddy cheeked, horny handed farmer smelling faintly of cattle and silage – that sort of thing.'

'But they didn't, did they? They thought breakfast would be in a nice room which smelt of nothing but furniture polish and bacon and eggs.'

'They didn't all ask for their money back. We'll get it right next year. Now listen – I've got this great idea for free-range Easter eggs...'